THE WORLD : Its Creation and Consummation

KARL HEIM

THE WORLD:
Its Creation
and Consummation

The End of the Present Age and
The Future of the World in
The Light of the Resurrection

Translated by ROBERT SMITH

MUHLENBERG PRESS
PHILADELPHIA
1962

A translation of the second German edition of *Weltschöpfung und Weltende*, published in 1958 by Furche-Verlag,
Hamburg, as Bd. VI of *Der evangelische Glaube und das
Denken der Gegenwart: Grundzüge einer christlichen Lebensan-
schanung*, by Professor Karl Heim.

AMERICAN EDITION
First Published 1962

Library of Congress Catalog Number 62–9748

Translation © 1962, Oliver & Boyd Ltd.
PRINTED AND BOUND IN GREAT BRITAIN BY
HAZELL WATSON AND VINEY LTD
AYLESBURY AND SLOUGH

TRANSLATOR'S PREFACE

The translator welcomes this opportunity of acknowledging his debt to the late Professor Karl Heim, whose lectures on science and religion he heard as a student of Tübingen University in 1932–33.

This volume deals with a wide range of sciences from astronomy and physics to geology and biology, and thus presents difficulties of translation which will not escape the specialists in these subjects. I am particularly grateful to those who helped me with some of these problems. The physics section was kindly read by my friend Mr Lewis Elton, PhD., of Battersea College of Technology who suggested some technical corrections. A considerable number of other improvements were suggested in the course of revision by the editorial staff of Messrs. Oliver and Boyd, and for their most efficient help I also express my thanks. Whatever errors remain are due to the limited knowledge of the translator.

Acknowledgments are due to the following for permission to reproduce material from the publications referred to:

Endeavour (article by Sir Harold Spencer Jones); Gustav Fischer Verlag (G. Heberer and F. Schwanitz, *Hundert Jahre Evolutionsforschung*); The Hogarth Press Ltd (Rainer Maria Rilke, *Selected Works*, trans. J. E. Leishman); Routledge and Kegan Paul Ltd (C. von Weizsäcker, *History of Nature*, trans. F. D. Wieck).

The Scripture quotations in this book are from the Revised Standard Version of the Bible, copyright 1946 and 1952 by the Division of Christian Education, the National Council of the Churches of Christ in the U.S.A., and used by permission.

R.S.

PREFACE TO THE SECOND
GERMAN EDITION

The first edition of this book appeared five years ago. Since then atomic research has indeed made further advances, and the most recent experiences which we are now witnessing give us the hope that new knowledge about the nature of the stars is imminent. But the views of the natural scientists about the beginning and the conjectural end of our world have, generally speaking, altered little in recent years. Thus it has not been necessary to make significant alterations of substance in the second edition.

Unfortunately the man who took the greatest trouble over the corrections which were needed in the new edition, Professor Otto Schmitz of Wuppertal-Elberfeld, has died in the midst of these labours. His departure has left a gap throughout the Evangelical Church in the Rhineland, and also in my life as a writer, in which he ever stood at my side as a true friend and counsellor. I can only look back in deepest thankfulness on what he was to me for many decades.

The thanks which I expressed in the first edition, to Professor Freiherr von Huene, Tübingen, Professor Lyra, Göttingen, and Dr Heinrich Herrmann, Tübingen, for encouragement and suggestions, are here gladly repeated. I again owe special thanks to Professor C. Freiherr von Weizsäcker and his publishers for allowing me to reproduce here some pages from his book *Die Geschichte der Natur*.

In conclusion I must express my heartfelt gratitude to Pastor Heinrich Schulte of Tübingen, who, in the place of my departed friend Otto Schmitz, has been a most valuable collaborator in revising and correcting this new edition.

The consolidated index to the complete work, which in the previous edition appeared in this sixth volume, will shortly follow as a separate publication.

KARL HEIM

Tübingen, January 1958

CONTENTS

ix

Paul sees in the Satanic power of sin an unsolved and humanly
insoluble mystery, which has subjected the whole of creation to corruption and death.

The only escape from the nihilistic mood underlying our civilisation,
which depends on natural science, is the Easter faith of the early
Church, which depends on divine revelation. This rests on two cosmic
facts: 1. The fall of the original creation into corruption through
original sin; 2. the new creation through the risen Christ. . . . The
transition from the unredeemed polar state of the world to the redeemed supra-polar form of existence has already begun. . . . The date
and the method of perfecting is reserved to the power of almighty God,
but is insoluble for natural science.

The six volumes of "Der Evangelische Glaube und das Denken der
Gegenwart" seek to provide in the conflict between faith and un-
belief a witness to the redeeming power of Christ which brings about
the perfecting of the world.

PART ONE

THE ORIGIN OF THE WORLD

CHAPTER 1

THE SCIENTIFIC VIEW OF THE ORIGIN OF THE WORLD

I. *The Size of the Universe*

IN the preceding volume of this work[1] we traced the transformation which is taking place in every department of natural science today. This involved us in the investigation of a number of special problems. Now we must extend our field of vision to the universe as a whole. Just as a visitor to an ancient cathedral, after spending some time in admiring a small carving on the high altar which was specially characteristic of the style of the building, might step out into the open space in front of the cathedral and take his stand at a distance, to get a general impression of the whole; so now we stand under the dome of the stars, encompassing us on every side with their overwhelming splendour, as we might see them from a lonely hilltop on a clear winter's night. As we gaze we become aware of the pettiness of the objects of man's striving on this earth, compared with the vastness of the universe and the mighty processes which are going on in the cosmos.

The Milky Way, which trails like a white veil across the night sky, reminds us of a fact which has become generally known only in the last few decades. This fact must be our starting-point if we wish to get some idea of the immensity of the universe. Our sun, which supplies the energy for all life on our earth, is only one member of a lens-shaped island universe which forms our galaxy. We measure astronomical distances in light-years (L.Y.). Since light travels at the rate of 186,000 miles per second, one light-year equals approximately six billion miles. Measured in light-years, our galactic system has a diameter of about 100,000 light-years. It is a rather flattened

---

[1] *Die Wandlung im naturwissenschaftlichen Weltbild*, Hamburg 1951; Eng. edn. *The Transformation of the Scientific World View*, trans. W. A. Whitehouse, London 1953.

disc, which rotates in a period of 200 million years. This explains the impression of an illuminated ribbon running across the sky. It arises from the fact that we are situated in a cluster of stars in the form of a disc; therefore from our standpoint the stars appear very dense when we look in the direction of the equator of this flattened disc. On the other hand, when we look in the direction of the two poles of this disc, the stars are thinly scattered. The number of fixed stars, that is to say shining suns, belonging to this galactic disc of ours may be estimated at about 500 million. Our sun is only a comparatively small fixed star. Its situation is eccentric in relation to the whole galactic disc, about 30,000 light-years distant from the centre. The diameter of other suns is ten to thirty times as big, although there are some smaller.[2] The planets, that is to say the earths which revolve round these other suns, cannot be made visible even with the aid of our strongest telescope, because of their immense distance. But we may assume the possibility that there are other suns belonging to our galactic disc which have planetary systems. Thus the planetary system to which the earth belongs is perhaps only one among millions.

The events which take place on our earth become still more insignificant when we realise the further fact that even this galaxy, in which our little planetary system with its mother star, the sun, is being whirled round in the immense rotation period of 200 million years, is only one among a countless number of similar galaxies. Most of these galaxies are somewhat smaller than ours, and from the immense distance at which we see them they appear as spiral nebulae. Kant had already conjectured this,[3] but it is only in recent times that this

---

[2] It is to be assumed that the vast quantity of red dwarf stars, which the latest photographs show in the "neighbourhood" of the sun (on the galactic scale, that is), also fill other regions of the galaxy, where they are recognisable because of their distance from us. Cf. W. Becker, *Sterne und Sternsysteme*, 2nd edn. Dresden 1950, § 67.

[3] See Kant's *Cosmogony*, trans. W. Hastie, Glasgow 1900, p. 63: "It is far more natural and conceivable to regard them as being . . . systems of many stars, whose distance presents them in such a narrow space that the light which is individually imperceptible from each of them, reaches us, on account of their immense multitude, in a uniform pale glimmer . . . all this is in perfect harmony with the view that these elliptical figures are just universes and, so to speak, Milky Ways, like those whose constitution we have just unfolded. And if conjectures, with which analogy and observation perfectly agree in supporting each other, have the same

conjecture has become a certainty. The question was raised whether the nebulae, for example the nebula of Andromeda, are only clouds of gas within the galaxy, or whether they lie right outside our galaxy, and constitute new and independent galaxies. Some thirty years ago it was proved that the latter is the case. The final verification of this entailed a tremendous amount of work.

Four main methods have been applied to the measurement of distances in the universe. The first method is that of trigonometrical calculation with the aid of what is called the parallax. We can illustrate the meaning of this from the principle of binoculars. The natural binoculars, by which we estimate distances, are our two human eyes. With their co-operation we can see the world stereoscopically, and as a result are able to judge the distance of objects. Artificial prism binoculars, as used in the army, have the two sights removed further apart, so as to make it possible to estimate even greater distances. A further step is taken in the "earth's orbit telescope" which operates for the most part photographically. We make use of the fact that the earth in its orbit round the sun carries us a very great distance in a half-year. This makes it possible to observe the universe from two widely separated stations in space at the beginning and at the end of the half-year. If we put together the two pictures which we receive at the beginning and at the close of a half-year, the effect is the same as if we were using prism binoculars, the two arms of which were as far apart as the diameter of the earth's orbit. Thus we get the distance of a star when we measure the minute angle which appears to be subtended by the diameter of the earth's orbit (the axis of the ecliptic) from the star in question. According to a law of trigonometry, the angle is smaller in proportion to the distance of the star. With the aid of this so-called parallax definition our island universe has become to a large extent transparent. We can measure the angle of the particular star with delicate instruments, indeed almost to 0·01 seconds. For the star which is nearest to us, Proxima Centauri, this angle amounts to 0·765 seconds. This corresponds to a distance of

value as formal proofs, then the certainty of these systems must be regarded as established."

Cf. also W. M. Smart, *The Origin of the Earth*, Harmondsworth 1955, pp. 185ff.

4·3 L.Y., or 25 billion miles. Sirius, with a parallax of 0·371 seconds, is more than twice as distant.[4]

A second method of measuring distance is by calculating the intensity of radiated light, which diminishes by the square of the distance. This is applicable if we have reason to assume the intrinsic brightness of a star. The simplest way would be to choose the mean value of the intrinsic brightness of all known stars, but this applies only for the mean value of the parallaxes of a stellar region in the galaxy. There is a corresponding procedure for whole groups of island universes. This is the only way of arriving at figures for the most distant island universes. The distances can be classified more exactly when stars are so bright that their spectrum is distinct enough to be classifiable. Each of the ten classes into which spectra are divided, according to the type of their spectral lines, has on the average a different intrinsic brightness, by which its statistical parallax can be reckoned. A further group of methods is applicable when the phenomena of motions are adequately determined, either in the case of double stars or of moving star clusters.

To these four methods a fifth has been added, which is applicable only when we have already determined the distance of a certain star with the aid of the phenomena of motions. This is the Cepheid method. It depends on the fact that there are variable stars whose light changes in regular periods. One type of these variable stars is the star Delta in Cepheus. The law is as follows: the brighter such a star is, that is the greater the mean brightness of this variable star, the longer is its period. Stars having the same period, for example stars which complete their light-variation in three days, must therefore have the same intrinsic brightness. If, therefore, stars having the same period, whose light-variation is completed in the same time, appear to vary in brightness, then the variation of their apparent brightness can only be due to the fact that they are at a different distance from us. According to the law of optics the inverse ratio must be equal to the square of their distance. Thus if we know the distance of a variable star which is nearer to us, we can by this law calculate from it the distance from us

[4] See Bernhard Bavink, *Allgemeine Ergebnisse und Probleme der Naturwissenschaften*, 7th edn., Bern 1941, p. 293; Eng. edn. *The Anatomy of Modern Science*, trans. H. S. Hatfield, London 1932. Also W. Becker, *Sterne und Sternsysteme*.

in light-years of another variable star whose distance is still unknown.

By these methods of measurement the distances of stars have been determined up to many millions of light-years. When we stand in awe before the immensity of the universe, whose members are no longer the planetary systems but the spiral nebulae, the whole of our human history, which we proudly call world history, appears only as a tiny pulse-beat in the life of the cosmos. The new giant telescope of the Mt Palomar Observatory (200 in. in diameter) in the reflector of which the nebula of Andromeda extends to a diameter of 72 inches, has disclosed to the astonished eye of man deeper and deeper gulfs of cosmic space, so that it is estimated that up to 60 million nebulae ranging in size to the twenty-first class can be found in a photograph. The farthest distance of a nebula so far measured is 500 million light-years. It might be thought that if the universe is such a gigantic complex of nebulae, of such inconceivable dimensions, then we must simply say that the universe is infinite. This was the idea of which Giordano Bruno was the prophet in the Copernican age. He revelled in the idea of the infinity of the universe, and this led him to worship this infinite universe for its own sake, and so to identify the universe with God. He thus came into conflict with the Biblical view that God is something other than the world, that He transcends the world.

In the question of the finitude or infinitude of the cosmos there has been a significant change in the views of influential scientists in recent years. This has been made possible chiefly by the work of the great German mathematician Gauss, the founder of non-Euclidean geometry. Euclidean geometry assumed that space was endless, because nowhere in space does one encounter a limit. One can go as far as one likes in space, and nowhere does one find the famous "fence" or electrically-charged barbed wire. Nowhere is there an end. One can go on and on for ever. Every end is a new beginning. On the other hand, it has been said since Gauss that this boundlessness of our universal space is no proof of its infinitude. For it is quite possible to conceive of spatial areas which have no enclosing bounds, yet which have a quite definite area, for example, the surface of a sphere. This is not infinite in size. We can reckon how many square inches it contains. Yet it is so constructed that one nowhere comes to a limit.

Of course, the surface of a sphere is only a two-dimensional form. But what we see in this example can be transferred in thought to three-dimensional space. The three-dimensional space in which we live might be related to it in the same way. It might return in upon itself like the surface of a sphere. Of course we cannot conceive it, for our human mode of thinking is confined to three-dimensional space. Yet our mathematical thinking can transcend the limits of what we can conceive. There can be relations which are not conceivable, but are thinkable. For the mathematical formulae in which we express the structure of our three-dimensional space can be transferred without difficulty, with appropriate modifications, to more than three dimensions.

Now modern astronomy and physics have been led by this hypothesis of Gauss to a view in conflict with that of Giordano Bruno. The universe, this complex of galaxies, is indeed without limit, but nevertheless it may be finite in extent and may turn in upon itself. The attempt has even been made, fantastic though it seems at first sight, to "weigh" the universe on the basis of certain calculations of the mean density of universal space. The "weight" of the universe expressed in grammes amounts to one with fifty-five noughts following. And there is talk of a diameter of the universe of about 10,000 million light-years.

Thus instead of the monistic idea of the universe held by Giordano Bruno we have returned to the idea of a unified whole. It is no shoreless sea, but something self-contained, with a definite weight and a measurable size.

This view is not, of course, universally accepted by mathematicians and astronomers. If it should be confirmed, it would be of great significance for our view of the world. For there is an unbridgeable contrast between any finite number however high, and the infinite. Between a universe of the extent of billions of light-years, and the infinite, there is a qualitative difference. Compared with the infinite, all differences between finite quantities are relative. Compared with infinite space and infinite time, the difference between an inch and a million light-years, between a second and billions of years, is insignificant. For if the theory of relativity is right there is no absolute measure of space and time within the finite universe. According to the system of reference we may choose, or the state of motion in which the observer is placed, immeasurable stretches of time are compressed to seconds, or expand to immense durations. If then it turns out that the universe is an entity which turns in upon itself, which can be weighed and measured, then in spite of its unimaginable extent it nevertheless belongs to the category of the finite. In that case it is separated by an unbridgeable gulf from everything which belongs to the category of the infinite and eternal, which transcends all measurement and all spatial and temporal dimensions.

If the world is not infinite, but constitutes a self-contained entity, the question inevitably arises, where does this entity come from? It is the problem of the origin of the universe. With a monistic view of the world as a shoreless infinitude this question could be omitted, and one could simply say that the infinite universe renews itself every moment out of its infinite energy for ever and ever. It is endless in space, and therefore also without beginning and without end in time. If this dream of the infinitude of the universe has come to an end, we have revived in a new form the old question which once gave rise to the cosmogonies, the myths of the genesis of the world, and the creation stories of ancient peoples: whence comes this finite system which is the home of us all? It cannot have defined itself. It must have been defined in some way.

Since our vision has extended far beyond our solar system to the spiral nebulae, two questions can here be kept apart which were merged in one in the old cosmogonies. The first and narrower question is: when and how did our narrower home arise, the planetary system of which the sun is the mother star? The second question is more comprehensive: when and where was the whole universe born? We must start out from the narrower, more immediate question. For we have reliable material to give an answer only to this question. It is only here that we stand on solid ground of observation and experiment.

The meteorites, which are the building materials or fragments of other world systems that have strayed into ours, the spectro-analytical investigation of distant stars, and the physical knowledge of the construction of matter out of elementary

particles, suggest the probability that not only the other planetary systems of our island universe, but probably also the spiral
enbulae, are composed of the same chemical elements as our
world, and are moved by the same forces of gravity and conservation of energy, of radioactivity and radiation. If we can
lay down the laws to which the origin of our sun can be traced,
we can at the same time from this starting point make at least
a tentative attempt to explain the origin of the universe.

2. *The Origin of our Planetary System*

So let us first consider the question of the origin of our planetary
system. This is a task by itself, because we cannot observe any
other system so small as ours. If we wish to make a picture of
the process of evolution which gave rise to our world of planets,
and to do it by scientific methods, we cannot, of course, start
from nothing. For according to the accepted scientific law
nothing can be made out of nothing.[1] *Ex nihilo nihil fit.* We
must, therefore, assume as given some kind of primeval state; we
must suppose a quite definite initial stage of the world, and
definite energies which are contained in this stage and which
might produce a process of evolution. Our explanation of the
world accordingly depends on how we think of this primeval
state, and what energies we thus assume as given.

   The two outlines with which scientific cosmogony started,
Kant's *Allgemeine Naturgeschichte und Theorie des Himmels* ("Universal Natural History and Theory of the Heavens," 1755),
and Laplace's *Exposition du Systeme du Monde* ("Exposition of
the System of the World," 1796)[2] were based on the two oppos-
ing conceptions of the origin of our planetary system which
were possible for men at this time. They thus indicated the
directions which have been followed for a long time in constantly varying forms by all scientific theories of the origin of
the world. According to Kant the world grew in the beginning
out of "elementary raw materials" or, more exactly, out of
particles of the primeval material which today we call meteorites. According to Laplace, on the other hand, it grew out of

---

[1] The opposite view of P. Jordan in *Die Herkunft der Sterne*, Stuttgart 1947, is
only possible if Einstein's tensor for matter is replaced by that of Levi-Città,
which has not convinced others.

[2] See Smart, *The Origin of the Earth*, for the relation between Kant and Laplace.

a gaseous mass. According to Kant the evolution of the world began in the following manner. In the beginning there was a cloud of meteorites. The corpuscles of matter of which it was composed moved hither and thither in every possible direction. The particles travelling in opposite directions collided with each other and, as a result, lost their own velocity and kinetic energy. Therefore they were attracted, by the law of gravity, to the place where there was the greatest mass, and from which the greatest power of attraction was exercised. In this way a body was formed by degrees which grew bigger and bigger, like the snowball of an avalanche. This was what later became the sun. So long as the particles, which were still separate, moved in all directions at random, they collided with each other and mutually deprived each other of their kinetic energy. Thus their own motion was paralysed, and they were captured by the force of attraction of the central body and fell into the embryonic sun. Only the particles which did not collide, because they were not moving in opposite directions but in a similar direction, preserved their independence, or, according to the law of the parallelogram of forces, combined the forces of their motions and united with each other. Their orbits approached more and more to a common maximal plane, from which their directions of motion deviated less and less. This plane Kant called the "plane of relation." When the orbits of all the particles had converged in this plane, they no longer perturbed each other. The planets coalesced out of the masses which circled in the "plane of relation." The moons were produced out of the planets in a similar manner. This explanation of the world by Kant was the starting-point of all the various meteoritic hypotheses which arose in the nineteenth century.

The chief objection directed against this theory today is as follows: when a particle of matter approaches a heavy body, such as the sun or a planet, it is not, so far as we can ascertain, absorbed by it unless it directly collides with it. Rather it is dragged by the heavy body into a hyperbolic orbit in which, after passing through the perihelion, it again moves off a vast distance away from the central body. Thus if we start from Kant's assumptions, there would arise out of the original cosmic dust cloud not a sun with widely separated planets circling round it, but a central body round which circled a mass of planets very close to each other, with dense collections of small meteors in between. Even the region beyond Neptune would be filled with dust masses, for the planets could only capture an insignificantly small portion of the masses which are to be found here.[3]

A different starting-point from Kant's was offered, before there was as yet any gaseous theory, by the nebular hypothesis of Laplace, which is often mistakenly confused with Kant's explanation. According to Laplace there was in the beginning, not a dust cloud nor a mass of meteorites, but a ball of gas, extending beyond the orbit of the outer planets. This ball of gas turned round on an axis, just as the earth now does. During this rotation the ball of gas contracted. Besides this, the rotation of the huge ball produced a centrifugal force. At a certain stage of the contraction of this rotating ball, the centrifugal force at the equator became stronger than the force of gravity which held the parts of the mass together. In consequence parts of the mass had to be thrown off. At first they formed rings, which afterwards broke up and coalesced in the form of planets, and so went on rotating.

This nebular hypothesis, which has the advantage of being illuminating and easy to picture, has long prevailed in lay circles, and even to some extent among specialists. Every thinking man says to himself that it can hardly be a coincidence that the planes in which the planets have their orbits do on the whole coincide. It is true that Uranus and Neptune rotate in the opposite direction to the general motion of the solar system; also the ninth moon of Saturn, for example, "Phoebe," discovered in 1904, and the two outermost moons of Jupiter, circle round their planets in the opposite way. Nevertheless they say to themselves that these occurrences are only insignificant exceptions in comparison with the direction of motion of the overwhelming majority, and they must have some special cause which is still unknown. The fact that the orbital planes of all the rest of the planets and moons coincide with each other seems to point quite clearly to a common origin of the whole system.

Then came the Plateau oil drop experiment, an absolutely

[3] See F. Noelke, *Der Entwicklungsgang unseres Planetensystems.* Berlin 1930, p. 135.

amazing demonstration, especially for laymen. Plateau took a drop of oil, in the middle of which was a thin rod, and put it into a mixture of water and alcohol, the specific gravity of which was equal to that of the oil. The drop of oil took on the form of a sphere in consequence of the surface tension, and gathered symmetrically round the rod as axis. It could be increased in size by the addition of more oil. If the rod was made to rotate, the oil drop uncoiled, and soon formed a flat disc. If the rotation was slowed down again, a ring was torn off, which went on rotating in the alcohol solution and was permanent. In this way a whole series of planets could be produced. It was clear from the beginning that while this model gave a good illustration, the oil drop experiment could by no means be a proof of the Laplace hypothesis. For the ball of gas which Laplace assumed is held together by gravitation, while the parts of the oil globule are held together by cohesion and surface tension, that is to say by processes which are governed by quite different laws. Besides, little planets can only be produced out of the uncoiling oil drops by changing the speed of rotation. If the globule is allowed to continue rotating at the same speed, no rings and no planets develop, but the oil is gradually dispersed on all sides in fine drops. This fact, however, is no refutation of the nebular hypothesis, since Plateau's experiment was from the first not meant as a proof, but as an illustration. The difficulty which the Laplace theory involves arises at quite another point.

If we consider the orbital movements of the planets, we find that the angular momentum of the mass of the sun, for example, is only one seventeenth part of the angular momentum of Jupiter. And yet this planet is a thousand times smaller than the sun. Even if, as is assumed by Jeans, the interior of the sun rotates considerably faster than the surface, the angular momentum of Jupiter is still eight to ten times as great as the angular momentum of the sun, and the momentum of all the planets together amounts to fourteen to seventeen times the angular momentum of the sun. Thus the angular momentum of the planets is much greater than it should be, if their source of motion were due to the mass of the sun from which they had been thrown off.

Hitherto the attempt to remove the difficulties involved in

the Laplace theory has not been altogether successful. The attempt has indeed been made to reduce the discrepancy of the angular momentum by assuming that the mass of the sun, and in consequence also its angular momentum, had formerly been greater and in the meantime had diminished. But the planetary system is only some 1000 million years old, and during this time the sun could hardly have lost any considerable amount of mass, unless processes had been at work which are still unknown to us. Weizsäcker and his school are engaged in an attempt to show that turbulence processes are an adequate explanation.[4]

In these views of the evolution of our planetary system, the meteorite hypothesis and the nebular hypothesis, the concern from the first was not merely with the local question how the one solar system of our sun arose, which is of course our home in the narrower sense but which is only an insignificant part of the vast universe. Kant and Laplace from the first directed their attention to the origin of the whole cosmos. For both theories traced our planetary system back to a primeval state, out of which it was born without any external influence. It arose quite spontaneously, from forces latent within it, according to the nature of a closed system. It is otherwise with a second group of hypotheses about the evolution of our planetary system. In this second group, as Noelke expresses it, the planetary system is treated not as a closed system, but as an open system, subject to influences from outside, and formed and shaped by these influences until it has assumed its present form. This second class of hypothesis thus refers not to a primeval state out of which the worlds were born as from a maternal womb, but assumes that an environment was already there, encompassing on all sides our planetary system in its embryonic state. The question which this class of hypothesis seeks to answer is thus limited as follows: how was the child of our planetary system born out of the maternal body of the universe, under the formative influences to which it was exposed from its environment? How did it receive its particular form? The answers which were given to these questions are of cosmological

[4] *Zeitschrift für Naturforschung*, Jan. 1952, two contributions to number on Heisenberg. We must wait and see whether the doubts raised by F. Noelke in his last work (*Zeitschrift für Astrophysik*, xxv (1948), p. 58) will be set at rest.

interest only in so far as they allow us to draw conclusions about the primeval state of the whole universe.

According to the hypothesis of Chamberlin and Moulton[5] our planetary system is the result of an encounter between two celestial bodies which passed each other like two ships meeting in the ocean of the universe. The two bodies were already in the state of suns rather than of nebulae. Our sun encountered an alien star. But no catastrophic crash occurred. The alien body did not collide with the sun, nor ram it, but went past on its way. This encounter, however, did not occur without leaving some effect upon the sun. The alien body, by the power of its attraction, produced a high tide on the side of the sun which was turned towards it, and an almost equally high tide on the opposite side. Thus arose eruptions similar to the sunspots which we observe today, only on a much larger scale, so that great masses were thrown off. These masses, which were torn apart from the original mass by the attraction of the passing star, came into the orbit of the alien body and were drawn into it. This explains why the planets, which were formed by the condensations of the masses thus thrown off, all move in the same direction, and have orbital planes which more or less coincide.

The idea of explaining our planetary system from the encounter of the original sun with an alien star has been developed by Jeans.[6] According to Jeans, the masses which were torn off the sun by the alien body did not quickly solidify into meteorites, as Chamberlin and Moulton thought, but remained in a gaseous state for a considerable time. Hence arises a possible explanation of the different sizes of the planets and of their various orbits, which he envisages as follows. The star as it passes must draw near to the sun and move away from it again. The closer its approach to the centre of the sun, the more quickly must the ejection process so produced have taken place. The rate of expulsion thus rose during the encounter from zero to a maximum, which was reached at the moment of greatest proximity to the alien body, and then was reduced

[5] For the whole subject see H. Jeffreys, "The origin of the solar system," in *Proceedings of the Royal Society*, A214 (1952), p. 281.

[6] J. H. Jeans, *Astronomy and Cosmogony*, 2nd edn. Cambridge 1928; *The Universe around Us*, 3rd edn. Cambridge 1933.

again to zero as it became more distant. If we think of the mass being flung off not as solid, but as gaseous, there would in this way arise, not a swarm of meteorites, but a long, continuous, gaseous strip. The mass of this strip was densest at the centre, for that was the part which arose when the passing star was nearest to the sun. The density of the mass gradually thinned out from this central point towards both ends. This strip of matter would lose heat by radiation like every other mass. During this loss of heat the ends of the strip would cool off and condense more quickly than the centre, for at the ends the surface was very great in proportion to the density. So the masses near the ends were more rapidly transformed into the liquid and subsequently into the solid state, while the centre of the strip still remained gaseous. Since the process of condensation within the strip took place at a varying rate, the effects of gravitation were various. Thus there arose knots in the strip, and finally it broke up into separate masses, which coalesced. During the formation of these spheres the ends of the strip, where the masses had cooled and condensed more rapidly, were transformed into the minor planets, while the centre, where the gaseous mass had not yet condensed, became the major planets. This explains why the planets are of unequal size, and why the two largest are situated at the centre. The eccentricity of the orbits of the planets is due to the fact that the tangential velocity, which the planets had acquired from the attraction of the alien star, was comparatively small. A resistant medium which surrounds the sun diminishes this eccentricity of the planetary orbits to a corresponding extent. Near the sun this resistant atmosphere was densest, and so the diminishing of the eccentricity was greatest. As a result the eccentricity of the orbits of Venus and the Earth is small, while that of Mercury is very great. This drama is repeated on a smaller scale in the origin of the Moon. The planet now plays the role which was taken by the sun in the birth of the planets, while either the alien body, or the sun, or both, take over the role of the perturbing body which produces the high-tide.

This hypothesis of Jeans has something attractive about it, but it does not quite satisfy our thirst for knowledge, chiefly because it does not trace back the origin of our planetary system to any law which is constantly observable. The world in which we live owes its existence to a rare chance, which may indeed have happened once, but of the occurence of which we can find no other instance. For if in the immense space of the universe, in which the stars are generally very far apart, two such bodies did come so near as would have to be the case here, it is an exceptional case, so rare that it would be rash to make it the basis of an explanation of the world.

With this we shall close our short account of the two main tendencies which have been followed since Kant and Laplace in explaining our planetary system. After all that has been said, it is understandable that since the end of the century-long monopoly of the Laplace hypothesis no other explanation of our planetary system should have won general acceptance, not even the most recent theory of F. Hoyle.[7] At the present time we have no uniform picture of the origin of our planetary system which still prevails in specialist circles. Neither the closed system, evolving spontaneously of itself, nor the encounter of the primeval sun with an alien body, has provided a basis of explanation on which research workers could agree. Science is thus more clearly conscious today than before that at this point too its capacity to explain these things is limited. We are not wholly in the dark, however. The main question which has divided the theorists since Kant and Laplace is the question whether the world had its origin in a swarm of meteorites or in a nebula. In the meantime, the progress of research into the cosmic nebulae has made it increasingly probable that the original state, not of our solar system alone, but of all solar systems, was a cloud of dust which arose out of a gaseous nebula. The great nebula of Orion, the nebula of the Pleiades, and the two nebulae of Cirrus in the Swan are ribbon- or flame-like agglomerations of nebulous matter, which assume the most varied forms. These nebulous structures exhibit striated condensations. In the arms of several spiral nebulae nodes of condensation can be clearly distinguished. These seem to be stars in process of evolution. We cannot, of course, inspect the details of any alien solar system, but we can guess that even outside our own system the stars are composed of condensed nebular matter, that each of the striated ribbons, which exhibit nodes of condensation, are in process of being

[7] F. Hoyle, *The Nature of the Universe*, Oxford 1950.

transformed into a system similar to our solar system. According to Noelke our solar system might have evolved out of a ribbon nebula in the form of an elongated S or the half of an S, belonging to a nebula which, like the nebula of Orion and the Cirrus nebulae, consisted of ribbon-like parts.[8] We can assume that the S-shaped primeval nebula of the solar system was not merely twisted in a two-dimensional plane, but like many snakes was also twisted sideways, and so formed a curve which can only be described in terms of three-dimensional space. In that case the four large planets, which show great similarities to each other, would be formed from the tail of the one S-curve, and the four smaller ones, which also resemble each other, from the tail of the other S-curve. The fact that the inclinations of the planetoid orbits amount to 30° or more might be explained from the deviation of the nebular curve sideways into the third dimension.

If the world at the ante-stellar stage of evolution first arose out of gaseous nebulae which were on the whole ionised, and not out of masses of meteorites or dust clouds, then certain other physical facts are of decisive importance for the understanding of the process of world evolution – facts which were still unknown in the time of Laplace, and to which attention has been called more recently, especially by Eddington, Nernst, and Alvén. The factors which are at work in the universe are not merely, as was previously assumed, forces of attraction, governed by the law of gravitation, and forces of friction, produced by a resistant medium. In addition, according to modern physics, there are two other new and important factors in cosmic evolution: radiation pressure and magnetism. This brings us to the discovery of an extremely important factor with which we have to reckon in explaining the evolution of the world. For it now appears that radiation pressure has a definite relation to the gravitation by which the component parts of a cosmic nebula attract each other. Radiation pressure together with the pressure of gas, and gravitation can at first balance each other. When this balance no longer exists, when radiation pressure diminishes, the gravitation by which the component parts mutually attract each other becomes stronger. Thus the parts grow together. In the interior of the nebula an

[8] F. Noelke, *Der Entwicklungsgang unseres Planetensystems*, p. 232.

increase of gravitation sets in, and with it a condensation. Jeans and Nernst indeed suppose that during this process in the nebulae the energy of radiation might be transformed into matter.[9] In the primeval state of the nebula, gravitation was thus less than it is now, and the system had not yet been so tightly compressed. The primeval nebula out of which our solar system arose must therefore have had greater dimensions than our planetary system today. It must have extended far beyond the orbit of Neptune. It may have exceeded the present magnitude of the system many times. Our solar system could have arisen in this way by condensation and decrease of radiation pressure in a primordial nebula, similar in extent to the ribbons in the nebula of Orion, the nebulae of Cirrus, or the other nebulae. It could thus, like these other nebulae which are actually found in cosmic space, have originally been in the form of a nebular arm of a similar elongated S-curve shape. The main mass of the nebula would have condensed to form the sun; the remoter parts would have evolved into planets. Out of the whole nebula one can think of a star-cloud evolving. In this way the above mentioned hypothesis of world evolution would be confirmed from a new angle.

We reproduce here a report by Sir Harold Spencer Jones of a theory of Baron C. von Weizsäcker:[10]

"It is a modification of Kant's theory, and assumes that the primitive Sun was surrounded by a rotating shell, consisting of an aggregation of atoms and smoke particles, of total mass about one-tenth the mass of the central Sun, in which each particle moved round the Sun in an independent orbit. The composition of the cloud is of hydrogen and helium and about 1 per cent. of heavier elements.

"Internal friction within the cloud will change the shape and orientation of the orbits of the various particles until they are eventually reduced to orbits of nearly circular shape in the neighbourhood of the Sun's equatorial plane; the envelope would then be in the form of a disk whose diameter is comparable with the present diameter of the solar system, and whose thickness is less than one hundredth of the diameter. The disk

---

[9] The new spinor theory of light advanced by Heisenberg and Wildermuth (*Annalen der Physik*, 1951) makes this opinion somewhat more probable.

[10] "The origin of the solar system," in *Endeavour*, x (July 1951), pp. 124ff.

consists mainly of gas, interspersed with a much smaller quantity of smoke particles, each particle moving practically in an independent gravitational orbit. It would be in a temperature equilibrium, there being a balance at any part between the energy received from the Sun and the energy radiated, so that the temperature would not be greatly different from the present planetary temperatures.

"Viscous forces would tend to equalize the angular velocities, slowing down the faster-moving inner parts and speeding up the slower-moving outer parts of the disk. The inner parts, as they slowed down, would fall nearer the Sun, while the outer parts, as they were speeded up, would move further away. This process brings about a gradual transfer of angular momentum from the inner parts of the system to the outer. There would be a gradual dispersion into interstellar space of the hydrogen and helium in the outer portions of the envelope, carrying away the troublesome angular momentum that would have had to be accounted for if the material had fallen into the Sun. It is the mass with low angular momentum that falls into the Sun. Weizsäcker computes that the original density of the envelope would be reduced to the present density of interplanetary space in about 200 million years, which explains why the envelope is not in existence today.

"Weizsäcker then considers how quasi-steady states, requiring but little energy for their maintenance, could be formed in the material round the Sun. A group of particles having orbits with the same period of revolution and semi-major axes, but with different eccentricities, will appear, when viewed from axes rotating with the common period, to be describing about the moving origin small ellipses which have a common ratio (2:1) of major axis to minor axis, the minor axis pointing to the Sun. They will therefore form a sort of vortex in the rotating system, in which the circulation is in an opposite sense to that of the rotation of the gaseous disk. The vortex can capture other particles only if their angular momentum lies below a certain threshold value, so that there must be an upper limit to its size. If the maximum eccentricity is $\frac{1}{3}$, Weizsäcker shows that five such vortices can be fitted into the annulus round the Sun. A stable arrangement is provided by a series of such annuli, each revolving round the Sun, the ratio of the radii of two consecutive annuli then being found to be constant. The radii of the rings consequently follow a law which is a close approximation to Bode's law.

"With such a distribution of vortices, there are steep velocity gradients in the neighbourhood of the circles between successive rings of vortices. Large viscous stresses will be set up, and secondary eddies, which may be regarded as in the nature of roller bearings, will form around the rings. The circulation in these eddies will be opposite to that in the vortices and therefore the same as the direction of the disk. It is found that the conditions for condensation would be more favourable in the roller bearings than in the vortices. The process of condensation has been studied in some detail by ter Haar. Condensation can occur only if the vapour pressure of large particles is less than the pressure in the gas, so that more atoms will condense on the particles than will evaporate from them. The nature of the condensation particles is determined mainly by the temperature; it is found that in the outer regions compounds like water, ammonia, and carbon dioxide can condense, but that in the inner regions only the metals and inorganic compounds which are heavier and less abundant can condense. Thus in the first stage of the condensation, the nuclei which form on the inner rings have higher densities than those which form on the outer rings. The second stage consists in growth by accretion of impinging particles sticking to the nuclei; which will occur more rapidly in the outer rings than in the inner. The final stage is the growth by gravitational capture; mainly of lighter elements, which is almost limited – as ter Haar shows – to the outer bodies only; this gravitational capture, mainly of the lighter elements, will still further accentuate the difference in the mean densities of the outer and inner condensations.

"Weizsäcker calculates that the growth of condensations, practically up to the limit at which no small particles were left, would take about a hundred million years, which is comparable with the dissipation period of the gaseous envelope. The condensations formed in the roller bearing eddies are the protoplanets. It is not clear, however, why there should be only one planet on each ring. Weizsäcker supposes that the condensations along one ring will come together 'in a manner difficult to visualize'; there would probably be interaction with the material in the wedge-shaped regions between the vortices, and a tendency for the adjacent condensations to approach each other.

"ter Haar finds that the condensation process gives a mass distribution which agrees with the actual distribution in the solar system as well as can be expected from general considerations. The only serious disagreements are that the mass of Mars is much smaller than the theory requires for a planet at the distance of Mars from the Sun, and the theory requires a planet between Mars and Jupiter; the asteroids, however, may be fragments of such a planet which has disrupted. The slowness of rotation of the inner planets can be adequately ascribed to tidal friction, caused by tides raised on them by the Sun.

"The formation of the so-called 'regular' satellites can be attributed to an analogous process of condensation inside the planetary atmosphere; the relative distances of the satellites follow laws of the Bode type. The 'irregular' satellites, viz. the Moon, the two satellites of Mars, and the outer satellites of the major planets, are assumed to be condensation products that were captured by the planets at a later stage. Gravitational capture would not have played any significant role in the building up of the regular satellites because of their small mass, which accounts for the observational fact that their densities are higher than the densities of their primaries, but lower than the densities of the inner planets."

Weizsäcker's theory therefore offers a plausible explanation of the principal features of the solar system.

3. The Origin of the Universe

All this has given us only a short survey of the present position of research into the origin of the solar system, which is our home in the narrower sense. In the course of this survey we have seen that now, as a result of the advance of physical observation, we know somewhat more than in the time of Kant and Laplace about the forces which caused this evolution, and we can also trace the development of our planetary system back for a considerable period. But in the end we are confronted with a gaseous nebula. In the bosom of this original nebula the seeds of all the future evolution of the world lie dormant. In it must lie, especially for the determinist, all the later events of

world history, including the history of our earth, the origin of
life, and finally the evolution of man – all these are present as
hidden potentialities of evolutionary development.

How did this original nebula, so vital for the future, so
fraught with destiny, come into being? And what is the position when we look out beyond the circle of our solar system,
and ask the more comprehensive question: How did the whole
universe originate? We may assume that the other celestial
bodies which are to be found outside our solar system, consist
of essentially the same chemical elements as our planetary
system, and that the same energies are operating in them as
we observe in our narrower environment. In that case the
methods which we employed in the first place to determine the
age of the celestial bodies have a universal significance. Within
our solar system we have a fairly sure means of finding out the
age of the celestial bodies. This is the decay of radium in radioactive substances, for which the period is measurable. Stones
containing radioactive substances have been examined to find
out the loss which has already taken place. From this can be
reckoned how long a time has elapsed since the stones were
formed. We talk of "stone clocks" in the geological strata,
which go on ticking uniformly through the millions of years of
the earth's history, and by which we later wanderers on the
face of the earth can see and read the time. From these clocks
we learn that our earth, according to the oldest geological
strata, is about 1500 million years old, probably even older,
but at all events not more than three times this age. Now we
may assume from what has already been said that the earth
must at one time have been separated from the mass which
forms the sun. Spectral analysis has shown that the sun contains
no substances different from those in our earth, although it
does contain them in different frequency. In this way a process
has been arrived at whereby the age of the sun can be estimated
from the comparison of solar and terrestial substances, and at
least for a certain part of the sun the figure of 4600 million
years is the result. The sun is thus not so very much older than
the earth. The meteorites too, those fragments of celestial bodies
which may well come from more distant regions of the cosmos,
have been investigated with the aid of radioactivity. From this
it has emerged that they are never substantially older than the

sun or the earth. No celestial body, so far as we know, has proved to be older than 10,000 million years. Now other spiral nebulae outside our island universe may be still older. But – this is the decisive point – all the light that we can throw on the subject points to the conclusion that even the bodies which lie outside our galaxy, supposing they should prove to be older than our island universe, nevertheless once had a beginning. They have not been in their present state from all eternity. The idea of a beginning of the world, of an origin of the universe, thus comes once more plainly in view for the natural scientist. The bold dream of the philosophers that the world is eternal seems to have become improbable today.[1]

There is another scientific fact, independent of this, which points in the same direction. This is the astonishing fact that the size and extent of the universe do not remain constant. The universe is expanding. It is true that a world catastrophe through contraction is conceivable, but the course of the world hitherto indicates expansion. When we observe a remote spiral nebula and analyse the light which comes to us in a spectrum, the lines of the spectrum show a so-called Doppler effect. What does this mean? When an express train travels towards us blowing its whistle, we hear a higher note than when it is travelling away from us. The explanation is quite simple. Because the whistle is approaching my ear, every second my ear is struck by a greater number of sound waves than when the locomotive is standing still or travelling away from us. The more numerous the sound waves that strike my ear every second, the higher the note. An analogous phenomenon occurs with light. This can be seen from an alteration of the spectral lines. They show a red displacement, which increases with the distance. In this way we can ascertain that the distant spiral nebulae are flying away from us, and at a tremendous rate, some of them at a speed of over 26,000 miles a second. Thus the universe, or the space occupied by the universe, is expanding,

---

[1] Here we must add a point that has come to light only recently. For some time there was a marked discrepancy between the age of the universe of 1150 to 1710 million years, as determined by a somewhat smaller diameter of the universe and the velocity of recession, and the age approximately twice as long, as determined by the abundance of radioactive substances and their decay products. Alfred Behr showed in 1950 that astronomical distances had probably been underestimated by a factor 2.2, mainly because the dwarf stars had been left out of account.

and at an enormous speed. The distance between the island universes increases in proportion to their remoteness. In estimating this increase many research workers have reached the conclusion that the diameter of the universe is increasing with the speed of light. If we wish to illustrate this pictorially, we may imagine a balloon inflating itself, or a deflated rubber ball expanding. This leads to a conclusion which is of great importance for our problem. From the process which is now taking place before our eyes, we can draw conclusions about the process which has been going on up till now in the universe. If the diameter of the universe is increasing, it must formerly have been smaller than it is now. So once it was very small indeed. If we reckon backwards, we come to a starting-point at which the expansion began. Ten thousand million years ago the diameter of the universe, which has increased to 10,000 million light-years today, was quite small, almost equal to nothing. 10,000 million years ago, therefore, the universe was at zero. This agrees remarkably with the estimate of the age of the universe to which we have been led by the measurements of radioactivity. When we read the "stone clocks" based on the loss of radium in the sun, earth, and meteors, there is evidence that no celestial body proves to be older than 10,000 million years. Lemaître, a Belgian scientist, says that 10,000 million years ago the universe, which was quite small to begin with, was produced by a primitive explosion. This was the moment in which atoms, stars, and galaxies were born. Indeed at that time space and time themselves were born. Since then the universe has been growing with tremendous rapidity. The universe can thus be compared to a sphere, such as can be seen in a great firework which is produced when a small, power-packed body explodes and produces an ever-expanding ball of light; or to a grenade, which bursts on impact and with a tremendous detonation disintegrates into minute fragments. This primitive explosion, from which the universe had its origin, would thus have occurred 10,000 million years ago, and we are still living in the midst of its effects. The riddle of world evolution might then be summed up in this question: What existed at that stage in the very beginning, which may lie more than 10,000 million years back? What existed at the moment when the first explosion occurred and the world grenade burst, the fragments and splinters of which have since then been flying off in all directions as galaxies, with colossal rapidity; and how did this first explosion come about?

According to Gamow[2] the material which existed in the beginning consisted of neutrons at a temperature of 1000 million degrees. At this temperature the production of all the chemical elements from neutrons is possible, since it is not so high that the atomic nuclei would distintegrate, and yet high enough to prevent the dissolution of the nuclei through the capture of neutrons. Neutrons decay (with a half-life of twenty minutes) into protons and electrons. Protons join with neutrons to form deuterons. In a similar way all the thousand and one sorts of atoms known today will have arisen, of which the three hundred "stable" atoms are preserved, while the others provide Lemaître's "firework." Their relative abundance must, according to Gamow, be in inverse ratio to their average efficiency in capturing the faster neutrons. So far as is known to date, this is the case with stellar and interstellar matter, and so also with the primeval nebula from which resulted, according to March,[3] first of all the formation of suns, and then through continual expansion their separation into island universes.

4. Man's Ancestry as seen by Natural Science

Let us look back at the long pedigree of modern *homo sapiens*.[1]

[2] See G. Gamow, "On relativistic cosmogony," in *Review of Modern Physics*, XXI (1949), p. 367.

[3] Arthur March, *Der Weg des Universums*, Bern 1948, p. 50. The theory described on pp. 29ff., according to which the hydrogen of the stars might also have collected around dust, seemed for a time to be confirmed by the supposed discovery of globules of dark cloud in the galaxy, which were regarded by Spitzer, Whipple, and Bok as transitional stages in the evolution of the stars. This view is found in Otto Struve, *Stellar Evolution*, Princeton 1950, pp. 103ff., and in a short notice in Hermann, "Eine kosmogonische Anwendung der hyperbolischen Keplerbewegung," in *Der mathemathische und naturwissenschaftliche Unterricht*, III (1950), p. 195. Meanwhile more critical views have shown that the globule form was an illusion. According to P. Jordan, *Schwerkraft und Weltall*, Brunswick 1952, p. 168, the objects are more like small clouds due to explosions.

[1] I am indebted for the details in this section to the palaeontologist Friedrich von Huene, and refer to his book *Die Erschaffung des Menschen, sein körperliches, seelisches und geistiges Werden*, Frankfurt 1952; also his *Weg und Werk Gottes in Natur und Bibel*, 2nd edn. Siegen and Leipzig 1949. To illustrate the discussion which follows we also reproduce two diagrams, the first of which was drawn on Professor von Huene's instructions at the Tübingen Palaeontological Institue. The second is taken from Gerhard Heberer, *Neue Ergebnisse der menschlichen Abstammungslehre*, Göttingen 1951, by permission of the publishers, Musterschmidt Verlag.

The views which were formerly represented by Steinmann, Klaatsch, Westenhöfer, and Dacqué have been superseded by later discoveries in recent years. Nowadays Man's family history is seen more or less as follows. We must start from the mammals, which begin in several lines at the border of the Triassic and Jurassic Ages. The most important line is that of the insectivores, which had already begun to appear in the Cretaceous Age. From these branched off, in the oldest Tertiary period, the predatory animals among others, and also the monkey-like mammals, the primates. In the Eocene period the half-apes or lemurs, which still live today in Madagascar, diverged from the primitive primates. In the Oligocene period there sprang from the main stem of the primates the *Simiae* or long-tailed apes on the one hand, and on the other hand the gibbon-like man-apes from *Propliopithecus*, known to us from Egypt. A descendant of *Propliopithecus* in the Lower Miocene Age is East Africa's *Proconsul*. Here there is another ramification. At this point the orang-like man-apes divide off, and also *Dryopithecus* in the Upper Miocene Age. From this date onwards the summoprimates are reckoned. From the *Dryopitheci* come on the one hand man-apes like the gorilla and the chimpanzee, and on the other hand the genuine hominids. During the Pliocene Age, lasting about ten million years, they developed an erect posture and other human characteristics. The first well-known hominids in the same half of the Pliocene Age are *Australopithecus* and *Plesianthropus* in the Transvaal. They have a height of about 4 ft. or rather more. At this point there appears on the border of the Pliocene and Quaternary periods *Australopithecus prometheus*, with steeper facial angles and a long, low skull. A little later we find in the Old Quaternary period the tall-statured *Paranthropus* (6 ft. 6 in. tall) with exceedingly strong teeth. He does not in fact belong to the main line leading to *homo sapiens*. On the other hand two important finds in southern Germany do belong to the main line, a jaw from Mauer near Heidelberg, from the earliest Quaternary period, and the middle Quaternary skull from Steinheim an der Murr near Stuttgart. Very similar to these South German finds is the *Pithecanthropus* from the earliest Quaternary period, which was found in Java and in China (Choukoutien near Peking), although it diverges somewhat from the main line and dis-

appears in the middle Quaternary period. The *homo* of Steinheim stands roughly at the point where Neanderthal man
branched off, in the cultural period of Le Moustier, about
300,000–150,000 years ago. Neanderthal man is distinguished
by deep eye-sockets and flat skulls, as well as by clumsy skeletons
and long extensions of the cervical vertebrae. Neanderthal man
is no more in the main line than *Pithecanthropus*. The main line
to *homo sapiens* begins in the early Quaternary period with the
discovery from Kanam at Lake Victoria in East Africa, and
is followed in the middle Quaternary by Kanjera, Swanscombe, and Fontéchevade, as well as by the skull from Steinheim (middle Quaternary), and in the later Quaternary period
by *homo sapiens*.

After this general survey, let us once more mention some
details which belong partly to the later period of the history of
culture. The remains of the skeleton of the South African
Australopithecus were found in extensive limestone caves. Beside
them lay whole heaps of bones of hunting trophies. It was
obviously a midden. There were antelopes, buffaloes, monkeys,
boars. All the skulls were split open in order to extract the
brains. Stone tools were not used; the antelopes' horns were
always broken off, perhaps to be used as daggers. The skulls
were split open with some two-pronged object, probably upper
arm or thigh bones with the two adjacent joints, which were
used as clubs. The hunting of the swift-running antelope
suggests planned co-operation and reflexion on the part of the
hunter. They could only be captured by divided forces from
an ambush.

The sub-human and early human types were alike without
chins. In the case of *Australopithecus* and *Plesianthropus* the
skeleton is human to a large extent; only the cranial capacity in
the skull is very small, 450 to 750 cubic centimetres (in *homo
sapiens* it is 1100 to 1800 c.c., average 1350 c.c.). From *Proconsul*
onwards the crown of the canine tooth diminishes, and in
Australopithecus it is already no bigger than the incisor. It gradually becomes like the pre-molars, but the roots remain relatively
strong. The bones of the extremities are slender and thin in
comparison with the man-apes. There is no trace of specialisation for climbing, but the first toe is still quite freely flexible.

Pithecanthropus was found in Java by Dubois in 1891. Königs-

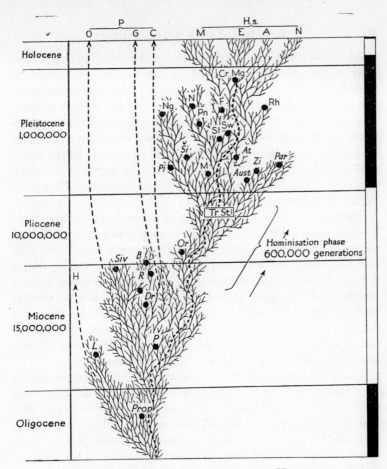

MODERN SCHEME OF THE EVOLUTIONARY HISTORY
OF THE HOMINOIDS

P = Pongidae; O = Orang-utan; G = Gorilla; C = Chimpanzee; H.s.=Homo sapiens; M=Mongoloids; E=Europoids; A=Australoids; N=Negroids; Cr Mg=Cro Magnon; Ng=Ngandong; N=Neanderthal; F=Fontechevade; Rh=Rhodesia; Pn=Preneanderthal; St=Steinheim; Sw=Swanscombe; Pi=*Pithecanthropus* Si = *Sinanthropus*: M = *Mauer*; At = *Atlantropus*; Aust = *Australanthropus* (*Australopithecus*); Zi = *Zinjanthropus*; Par = *Paranthropus*; Tr st = Transitional stage; Or = *Oreopithecus*; Siv = *Sivapithecus*; B = *Bramapithecus*; R = *Ramapithecus*; Dr = *Dryopithecus*; H = Hylobatids; L = *Limnopithecus*; P = *Proconsaul*; Prop = *Propliopithecus*.

The dotted line shows schematically the ancestral line of *Homo sapiens*. On the right is shown the relative length of the ages in the history of the earth: reading from the top, Holocene (black), Pleistocene (white), Pliocene (black), Miocene (white), Oligocene (black, not complete).

After: *Hundert Jahre Evolutionsforschung*, edd. G. Heberer and F. Schwanitz, 1960.

wald found three other skulls there in the years 1936–9. They have a flat, receding forehead, a cranial capacity which is already larger than in *Australopithecus* and *Plesianthropus*, 750–1300 c.c. Here the skeleton is already completely human. Remains of over fifty individuals (including the Chinese specimens) are known at this stage. The climate must have been dry. In North China there was desert with loess dust. In the caves were found countless beasts of the hunt, 70 per cent of which were deer. The bones show traces of craftsmanship. Many are burnt. In Choukoutien fireplaces with charcoal were found. Numerous pieces of quartz were discovered which had been brought from a distance; many were crudely worked and showed traces of edging and sharpening. These men thus used tools and fire, which no beast had ever done. The fire was no doubt first of all taken from steppe fires, and this demanded human courage and reflexion. It was first received and later manufactured by man himself by the production of sparks. Thus for the first time a power of nature was taken by man for his own use. The lower jaw from Mauer, near Heidelberg (*"homo heidelbergiensis"*) seems to be similar to *Pithecanthropus*.

The skull remains from Swanscombe, which were found on an upper terrace of the Thames, lead us a step further. This skull has a cranial capacity of 1300 c.c., is 250,000 years old, and derives from the Riss-Würm interglacial period (along with *Elephas antiquus*). It had a domed forehead. Near it were found stone tools of the Acheulean culture. The skull of Fontéchavade in eastern France, found in 1949, as well as the Steinheim skull and a find at Ehringsdorf in Thuringia, date from the same age. They have actually a brain capacity of 1450 c.c. Stone tools of the Mousterian culture belong to them.

From Java and from South China human jaws and teeth have been reported which suggest a size double the normal. The Bible also tells of the gigantic Anakites and Rephaiim (Num. XIII.33; Is. XIV.9) of whom the reporters say: "We seemed to ourselves like grasshoppers, and so we seemed to them." Goliath too was descended from such a race of giants. According to the Biblical account he was six ells and a span, that is 13 ft. 6 in. tall. His brother was of a similar height. Something similar is told of King Og of Bashan, whose iron bedstead is reported to have been over sixteen

feet long. So he himself must have been twelve to sixteen feet
tall.

In our time such giants are rare exceptions. There lives in
London, for example, a man who is 9 ft. 4 in. tall, and who is
still growing. At Pegu in Lower Burma there lives a man called
Toluka, born in 1922, who is 9 ft. 9 in. tall.

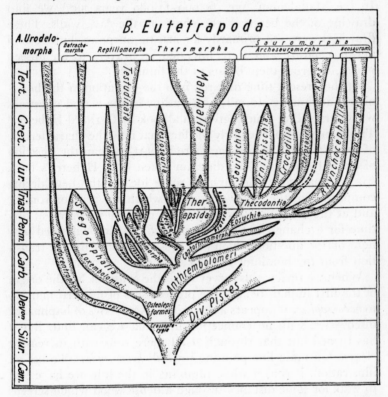

As regards the stages of culture, they are named after the
stone tools in France. They are classified as Chelle, Acheuil,
Le Moustier, Aurignac, La Madelène; then follows, after the
Quaternary period, the middle and late Stone Age or the
Neolithic Age, which lasted in the Orient from 6000 to 4000
B.C. In the Neolithic Age plants were cultivated and domestic
animals were bred, which did not occur before.

The high level of culture is shown by the fact that now there
appear signs of belief in the survival of life after death. This is

seen in a primitive cult of the dead. Burial took place and tombstones were erected. Gifts were laid beside the bodies, consisting of stone tools and provisions; it was thought that the dead lived on in a new form. This happened in the Mousterian Age (about 300,000–150,000 B.C.). Then came the Aurignacian Age, which is estimated as 150,000–60,000 B.C. In the Madalenian Age (60,000–11,000 years B.C.) we find drawing of the beasts of the chase on the cave walls. These drawings were not primarily for artistic purposes, but were of a ritual nature and were intended as prayers to an unseen power, to bring these beasts to the hunter.

At the present time research into the evolution of the hominids is advancing stormily. An outline of the actual questions which are still at issue is given in a book by Gerhard Heberer.[2] This brings out particularly the fact that now the characteristic of erect posture has become more important than the question of cranial capacity. The diagram taken from Heberer's book (p. 31) may give the layman some idea of the bewildering complexity of the discoveries with which we are confronted, and at the same time shows that we must be prepared at any time for a change in the total situation, which will shed new light on the question which is of most interest to us, the transition from the hominids to *homo sapiens*.

When we review this survey of all the evidence for the origin of the first human beings, the predecessors of modern man up to *homo sapiens*, it appears at first sight like a series of haphazard discoveries, with no connecting link that we can find. But it has turned out that through it all there runs with increasing clearness a main line pointing towards *homo sapiens*. To use an illustration, it is as if while rambling in the hills we have had to walk for some distance through a dense wood which screens the view of the peak. But through this wood there also runs a path, indicated by red markings, which point the route to the summit. So, through the complex maze of fossil remains and discoveries which today are beyond the layman's power to grasp, there is an ever more clearly apparent main line, in which we can trace the footprints of the Creator, who has been preparing for thousands of years according to a certain plan for the appearance of *homo sapiens*, this lord of creation.

[2] *Neue Ergebnisse der menschlichen Abstammungslehre*, Göttingen 1951.

5. *The Place of Man in the Organic World*

When we review the completeness of the whole constitution of nature, the inorganic, the vegetable, and the animal worlds, finding their crowning fulfilment in Man, we notice at once that these three worlds do not exist side by side without connexion. They are intimately related. The vegetable world absorbs inorganic substances as nourishment in the form of mineral substances dissolved in water, the carbon from the air and the mineral salts from the earth, and with these builds up its living bodies. It thus lives on the thin covering of inorganic matter laid down on the solid rock formations of the globe after it had cooled. There are also, it is true, plants which do not live on inorganic substances, but on other plants, the vegetable parasites. But this exception only proves the rule. In contrast to the plants, animals cannot live on inorganic substances, but only on plants. The inorganic, the vegetable, and the animal worlds thus form a kind of economic partnership which is subject to the law of sacrifice and mutual help. The plants draw directly from the treasures of the soil in the inorganic world, they process their gains, and then at once offer them in full measure to the animal world for its nourishment.

How did this many-branched world of organic life come into existence, we ask, this world which reaches its climax in Man? Let us here summarise briefly the most important results of modern palaeontology, to provide a starting-point for the discussion of the fundamental questions with which we are here concerned. First of all, agreement has today been reached to a large extent with regard to the periods in which the rise of the organic world took place. This is the result of the application of two methods of calculating the geological periods, independently employed and mutually confirming one another. The "lead method," in which physical calculations are made to determine the date at which lead, the end-product of the decay of radium, came into existence in radium-bearing ores of various geological strata; and the "astronomical method," in which the variation in the amount of radiation which reaches the earth from the sun is estimated.

In the lead method, the incidence of radium-bearing ores in the various geological formations is noted, and the physically calculated figures are arranged according to the geological age of the ore. By combining the geological discoveries about the strata with the physical calculations, quite definite figures have been arrived at. About the beginnings of life, which have left only a few traces in the form of fossils in the pre-Cambrian Age, we can as yet make no pronouncements. But we know that the oldest fossil-bearing strata in the pre-Cambrian Age are about 1500 million years old. The beginning of the Cambrian, and so of the Paleozoic Age (Cambrian, Silurian, Devonian, Carboniferous, Permian) is 540 million years ago. Of the individual strata in the Paleozoic Age, the Silurian begins at least 450 million years ago, the Carboniferous 340 million years ago. The Mesozoic period (Triassic, Jurassic, Cretaceous) starts with the Triassic formation 200 million years ago. The Neozoic (Tertiary, Modern period: Diluvium, Alluvium) begins with the Tertiary 60 million years ago.

These estimates, arrived at by physico-geological methods, have been unexpectedly confirmed from the astronomical side. The Serbian astronomer Milankovič investigated in 1919 the variations in the amount of radiation reaching the earth from the sun on the basis of three variable quantities: the eccentricity of the earth's orbit, the variation in the angle of the ecliptic, and the displacement of the perihelion. He made his calculations first of all backwards for a period of 800,000 years, and reported his results graphically for the Quaternary period in the form of climatic curves. When the geologists saw these curves, they at once noticed that they bore a striking resemblance to the graphical description of the glacial and interglacial periods, which the geologists Penck and Brückner had already given some years earlier for the climatic fluctuations during the Ice Age in the Alps. Thus the calculations which had been instituted according to the lead method were continued for the most recent geological past.[1]

Now if we review, so far as is possible for us today, the mighty process of creation, which has been unfolding in the tremendous period of 1500 million years, we find it doubly astonishing. The history of life on this earth is not just a chaos, a confused and aimless criss-cross of conflicting tendencies.

[1] F. von Huene, *Schöpfung, prähistorische Menschenfunde und biblische Weltanschauung*, 1933; and *Weg und Werk Gottes in Natur und Bibel*, 2nd edn. Siegen 1949.

Rather it is controlled as a whole by a great plan and a uniform system. The history of life is divided into quite distinct periods, which follow each other and have a distant resemblance to the empires in the history of mankind, which according to the views of the Old Testament prophets emerge from the ocean and again subside. In each of these immense periods the geologists have recognised the animal and vegetable forms characteristic of each age. In the beginning there must have been a purely vegetable period of which the traces have disappeared. We must assume this, if only because animals could not have come into existence if plants had not previously existed. This vegetable period was followed first of all, in the Cambrian Age, by the period of the invertebrates, of which the highest class is represented by the crustaceans. Then comes the age in which the first fish appear. In the Silurian and Devonian Ages they are the highest animals. There are still no land animals. Then comes the age of the amphibians and reptiles in the Carboniferous period; the age of the reptiles, in which the Saurians took the lead, in the Permian, Triassic, Jurassic, and Cretaceous periods; then the age of the mammals in the Tertiary period and in the diluvial Ice Age. At the end of the age of mammals stands Man.

When these epochs are reviewed, we see in the second place that they form a uniformly ascending line. Each of these epochs, instead of being submerged in the next, survives, although no longer as the highest class, but in a subordinate form. Thus the picture which emerges reminds us of a seven-branched candle-stick. As a whole it does not make the impression of a haphazard process. It appears rather as a plan designed by a creative spirit. It may be compared to a drama in several acts, or to a musical composition in which, after the introduction, there follows an allegro, then an adagio and a scherzo, and lastly a finale. It may also remind us of the structure of a pyramid, in which the lower stratum always supports the next higher one which is superimposed on it. In the last act of the drama, in the finale of the composition, at the apex of the pyramid appears Man. The whole creation builds the gateway through which the king of creation can enter in. It erects the throne which in the end Man is to occupy. Thus all creatures work together to make possible the existence of this unique creature in whom the creation of the world is perfected.

The whole plan is not governed by the idea of democratic levelling and equality, but is designed according to the strict principle of selection. Everything is planned with the aim of endowing one creature with dominion over the earth, and so of carrying out the "Führer" (leader) principle all along the line. The whole design is given a tremendous dimension by the fact that it extends to a period of more than 1500 million years.

Now for the student of the Bible it is surprising that the building plan of the creation which is shown us by palaeontological research agrees in all essential respects with what is said in Genesis about the third, fifth, and sixth days of creation. On the third day of creation first of all the vegetable world begins. "Then God said, 'Let the earth put forth vegetation, plants yielding seed, and fruit trees bearing fruit in which is their seed, each according to its kind, upon the earth. And it was so'" (Gen. 1.11). After the fourth day of creation had been devoted to the making of the world of the stars, with the fifth day of creation begins the age of the fishes and then of the birds. "And God said, 'Let the waters bring forth swarms of living creatures, and let birds fly above the earth across the firmament of the heavens.' So God created the great sea monsters and every living creature that moves, with which the waters swarm, according to their kinds, and every winged bird according to its kind. And God saw that it was good. And God blessed them, saying, 'Be fruitful and multiply, and fill the waters in the seas, and let birds multiply on the earth'" (Gen. 1.20f.). On the sixth day of creation there followed after the age of the fishes and birds the age of the land animals that creep upon the ground in their various kinds and species, and last of all Man, to whom is committed the lordship over the animal world. "And God said, 'Let the earth bring forth living creatures according to their kinds: cattle and creeping things and beasts of the earth according to their kinds.' And it was so. . . . Then God said, 'Let us make Man in our own image, after our likeness; and let them have dominion over the fish of the sea, and over the birds of the air, and over the cattle, and over all the earth, and over every creeping thing that creeps upon the ground according to its kind.'" Probably the author of this simple story of creation thought of ordinary days. But what he describes is the pregnant summary of a total picture which, according to the results of geological research, evolved in a period of over 1500 million years.

Having regard to the great plan of creation of the living world, ascending in a line which reaches its peak in Man, let us discuss the three questions the answer to which decides the place of Man in the total world of life.[2]

1. The problem of the fact of descent, that is to say, the question whether descent does in fact prevail in the family tree of the living world, which we have to some extent surveyed on the basis of palaeontological discoveries. Do the branches and leaves of this tree simply make their appearance in succession as a result of separate acts of creation? Or do they stand in a genealogical relationship to each other? Do the more highly developed species (and races) derive from the lower? Has the whole tree grown from a single root?

Even this first question with which the family tree of the living world confronts us is decisive for the relationship of Man to nature as a whole. For if the genera and species of organic being do in any way at all derive from each other and go back to a common root, this principle of continuity has the result that even the top of this wide-spreading tree, the last transition from mammals to Man, has come about in the same way as all the many other transitions which have led from the crustaceans to the mammals. For the step from mammals to Man is from the biological point of view much shorter than, for example, the step from fish to amphibians, or from saurians to mammals. Thus if the steps which have led up from the invertebrates to the mammals are of a genealogical character, then it must be assumed in advance that the last step from mammals to Man must also have been a genealogical transition (see below, pp. 38ff.).

2. If this descent is affirmed in principle, the second question arises, which we must carefully distinguish from the first, the question of the manner of descent. How does the descent of different species from each other come about, and what are the factors which have produced it? Was a blind, mechanical law in control, or was there a purposeful inner growth amid

---

[2] Cf. the fundamental sections in B. Bavink, *Ergebnisse und Probleme der Naturwissenschaften*, pp. 494ff.

all the various influences of environment? Or must we combine both factors? Or are quite different forces at work, which we have only discovered as a result of modern biological research? According to the way in which we conceive of the manner of descent, the origin and the existence of Man appear in quite a different light. In the one case he is a product of chance, in the other the fulfilment of a plan, or the final working-out of a mysterious life force (see p. 48ff.).

3. Only when these questions are to some extent clarified can we approach the last, quite specific question, which has been the burning topic of philosophical controversy since Darwin. What is the position with regard to the descent of Man from the apes in the light of the most modern discoveries? In what genealogical relationship does *homo sapiens* stand to the species most closely related to him within the family tree, to the primates and summoprimates? (See p. 10f.)

We begin with the question of the fact of descent. This descent has not only been rejected on dogmatic grounds by religious fanatics, but has also been flatly dismissed on purely scientific grounds by some zoological experts. We mention here only Albert Fleischmann, a professor of zoology, who was convinced that the doctrine of descent rested from the very beginning on a misunderstanding of the nature of all exact science. An exact science, explains Fleischmann, does not start from general principles and derive the special cases therefrom by logical deduction. It demands rather that all its teaching should be based on incontrovertible facts of observation, and does not permit the reverse process by which conclusions are drawn from theoretical, general opinions, for which proofs are feverishly sought afterwards. The assertion of descent, if it is to be scientifically exact, must show that the living organisms have really transcended the limits of their type, not merely that we should find ourselves enlightened by the thought that they might have transcended them. For this purpose the provision of mediating links is indispensable. Now since the questionable transformation of the organisms from a single form must have taken place in a dim and distant primeval age, a demonstration of the forms of transformation cannot be carried out. The whole problem therefore lies beyond the realm of exact science, and it can only be dealt with by means of imaginative synthesis.

The principal defect of the evolutionary philosophy of nature would accordingly be that it confuses the products of our minds with natural phenomena. By the logical grouping of the various species, and by the arrangement of these species (in oral and written discourse) in a time sequence according to their relationship, we are misled into the erroneous opinion that the grouping in the system and the systematic sequence reveal a mysterious connexion. It is said, for example: there are flying mammals equipped with a parachute (the bats), and they are also climbers; therefore the ancestors of the bat were formerly climbers. There are simple and complicated eyes, therefore the ancestors of the vertebrates had simple eyes. There are mammals with short and long necks, therefore the giraffe's neck was formerly short. In this way evolutionary theorists assumed the role of poets, who in drama or epic seek to revive men's memory of a long-forgotten past by taking impressions derived from the facts and elaborating them in poetic form. In this way there arise phylogenetic accounts of as much value as the idea current in the Middle Ages, that the Franks were descendants of the Trojans, the Britons descendants of Brutus, the tyrant-hater. It is as if someone finding a corpse in a wood should elaborate from the sight of this totally unknown person the whole story of his life from the cradle to the grave.

As against this radical rejection, which banishes the whole idea of evolution into the realm of fable and fanciful speculation, we must point out a number of undeniable facts which are not speculative theories but realities. These facts are certainly not overwhelming proofs. But they do provide, for any unprejudiced person, impressive indirect indications of genealogical connexion and the relationship of the various species.

The first fact is the discovery of comparative anatomy, which every schoolboy knows today. If one compares the skeletons of different vertebrates (the lizard, the salamander, the mole, the eagle, the bear, the cat, the stag, the horse, the lion, the ox, the gorilla, the chimpanzee) the similarity of structure is at once noticeable. In every case we have the same bones, even though they have become deformed or atrophied in various ways. In the legs of mammals, in the wings of birds, the pinions of penguins, the burrowing-claws of moles, the same fundamental type always appears. This uniformity of structure leads us to the conclusion that these skeletons all belong to the same family. They are variations on a single theme. It is like the Gothic cathedrals of the Middle Ages, which all have the same ground-plan, the same vaulted construction and orna- mentation, so that the uniformity of the plan strikes the eye at once.

In addition to this anatomical similarity, there is a second and more important factor. This is the rudimentary organs. The eyes of the mole still lie under the skin in our species, as organs which have become incapable of functioning. Further, in the body of the whale there are still concealed the relics of hind legs. These indicate that they apparently had four-legged ancestors. Otherwise it is impossible to explain these redundant and useless parts of the skeleton. Where have these under- developed elements of the organism come from? If there is a genealogical connexion here, these marine creatures must have been descended from a wholly different species of organism, which walked on four legs. Here is evidence of a very decisive transformation in the evolution of the animal world.

The third fact, which points in the same direction, is the so- called biogenetic principle of Häckel, which is not indeed uni- versal, but is valid on the whole. According to this the develop- ment of the embryo is a summary recapitulation of the evolu- tion of the family in a brief review, right back to the fish stage. In the first phase the embryo of a human being looks like the embryo of a shark, a ring-snake, or a hen. The zoologist can, indeed, as Fleischmann justifiably objected, recognise even in the earliest stage to what species of creature the embryo belongs. Nevertheless, an obvious likeness is present. Only in the later stages does the human embryo pass through the reptile stage to the mammal, and finally to Man.

The fourth and most impressive fact is the so-called blood relationship, which Uhlenhuth and Friedenthal have established on the basis of blood reaction. We know, from the blood trans- fusions carried out in hospitals, that the blood of one human being can generally be mixed without difficulty with the blood of another belonging to the same blood group. The compati- bility of blood is a sign of kinship, of belonging to the same species. This is also expressed in the profound symbolism of the old Germanic blood-brotherhood. When, however, blood of a different species is injected into any creature, for example the blood of a human being into a guinea-pig, symptoms of poisoning at once begin to appear. The body of the affected animal protects itself by producing the so-called antibodies, antidotes, or anti-toxins, which render harmless the poisons which have penetrated the system and the noxious agencies producing them. Through these antidotes the organism becomes immune. These antibodies can be kept in a clear, colourless solution, if one frees the blood (by centrifugal force) from the red blood corpuscles suspended therein. This fluid is the blood serum. Through the protective antidotes contained in serum from guinea-pigs suitably treated beforehand, the foreign plasma is neutralised. This is shown by a cloudiness appearing in the guinea-pig serum. The foreign plasma is rendered harmless by being made into an insoluble sediment.

This reaction occurs only in the presence of the blood of some quite specific animal of a different species, with which the test animal has been treated beforehand. It is thus protected only against infection from the blood of that particular animal. But the reaction comes into operation in a correspondingly lesser degree in the presence of the blood of such species as are closely related to the alien creature with whose blood the test animal has been treated beforehand. In the case of a guinea-pig treated with dog's blood, the reaction also occurs, though somewhat more feebly, with the blood of wolves, and more feebly still with the blood of foxes and jackals. We have thereby obtained an excellent way of determining exactly the relationship between species. The greater or less degree of reaction is a measure of the nearness or distance of relationship of the species within the system.

This experiment has been made with the blood of human beings and apes. The distance between Man and the species of apes nearest to him has been measured by this test, and according to Mollison, whose findings have been adopted by H. Weinert, the results arrived at are as follows. If we denote the maximum of mutual transfusibility of blood by zero, and the deviation from this maximum by ascending numbers from one to infinity, we then obtain the following figures: Man 0–3; chimpanzee 9; orang-outang 17–18; macaque, long-tailed monkey, New World monkey, prosimian 50. Of course even the chemical similarity of blood is no real proof of descent from the same ancestor, and so of real "blood relationship." But it seems to us at least a very strong indication of such a connexion.

We have mentioned here only the most important facts which constantly suggest the idea of evolution: the anatomical structure of all higher animals, the rudimentary organs, the biogenetic principle, and the blood-transfusion tests. These facts are not in themselves a foundation secure enough to support such a colossal edifice as the idea that the manifold richness of the organic world has a common ancestry, and that the inconceivable variety of its forms must have evolved from a single root. All the daring conclusions which might be drawn from the above-mentioned facts collapse like a house of cards if it should turn out that a transition from one species to another, which must be assumed if all organisms have a common ancestry – a heritable mutation, that is, of specific character-istics – can be proved to be scientifically impossible. The radical critics of the idea of evolution like Fleischmann accordingly believed that the whole idea of evolution had been once for all refuted by a knock-out blow as the result of a single, funda-mental discovery of biology; namely, Mendel's law of heredity, which was supposed to prove experimentally that in all breed-ing it is always only possible to obtain new combinations of the hereditary characteristics already present in the progenitors but never a change of species.

At Brno in the 1860s the Augustinian monk Gregor Mendel carried out experiments in plant-hybridisation for eight years in complete privacy in his cloister garden of an area of only 220 square yards. In particular he crossed varieties of garden peas, beans and hyacinths, and investigated the products of the cross-fertilisation in the following year. He published the results of his experiments in two treatises which appeared in 1865 and 1869 under the title *Versuche über Pflanzenhybriden* ("Experiments with hybrid plants"). These little essays were hardly noticed in the high tide of Darwinism, which at that time had begun its triumphal march. It was not until 1900 that these works were rediscovered, and Mendel enjoyed a posthu-mous revival. He was celebrated at a scientific congress as "one of the great stars in the heaven of modern science." Mendel's discoveries are the foundation on which all modern study of heredity is built.

In his hybridisation experiments with 60,000 peas and other garden produce Mendel arrived at fixed numerical laws, which seem to be universally valid for the vegetable and animal world. In the present context it is enough to mention the simple, basic law exhibited with striking unanimity everywhere in the vegetable and the animal world, in exactly the same way in heredity experiments on banded and bandless garden snails as in those on white and red varieties of the Marvel of Peru, *Mirabilis jalapa*. The whole process may be expressed in letters as follows. If one inherited character (bandlessness, red-flowered) is designated by the letter A, the other (band, white flower) by the letter a, then on cross-fertilisation both inherited characters enter the fertilised egg-cell. We write the hybrids $= Aa$. At the third stage, through the chance encounter of the characters A or a, which are present separately in the sex cells, and are taken up into the egg- and sperm-cells, there arise the following combinations: egg-cells $(A + a) \times$ sperm-cells $(A + a) = AA + Aa + Aa + aa$. The plants with the formula AA or aa, in which the same hereditary characters are thus paired, flower red or white. From them again develop egg- and sperm-cells with the same hereditary characters. On inbreeding their heredity remains true. On the other hand, all plants with the formula Aa are of divided heredity. Of course, the process is much more complicated when not merely two, but many hereditary characters or genes are present, which enter into combination with each other. But if the law of heredity is confirmed under simple conditions, it can be assumed that it will apply with the same mathematical accuracy even in the combination of many hereditary characters.

The result of such heredity tests thus seems to be that nothing essentially new arises in the second and third generation, but only different permutations of the characters that are already in existence. The results of Mendel's research into heredity seem at first to call into question the whole idea of evolution. For although so many circumstances seem to point to a single ancestry for the organic world, the emergence of one species from another seems to be in contradiction to the exact and assured facts of the process of heredity. In that case, all observed facts leading to the idea of evolution would have to be explained in some other way. Everything here depends on the one question, which can be described as the most important question of modern biology. Is *mutation* possible, in spite of the results of the science of heredity? Is there any change in the hereditary constitution, which is not merely a new combination of the characters already existing, but a real change in the germ plasm? Given the present state of biological knowledge, what can we say about the question of the possibility of mutation?

The question at issue is much more clearly stated today than was possible in the time of Darwin, Weismann, and Häckel. The science of heredity and the investigation of chromosomes and genes have enabled us to make good progress at this point. We know that in plants and animals there are variations of different kinds which must be clearly distinguished. There are, first of all, the merely fluctuating variations, which are not hereditary at all, but only occur now and then (paravariations). These can be left out of account altogether for our purpose. Then there are the various Mendelian combinations (mixovariations). These may be very strong variations of colour and form (for example, white and red flowers, long and short leaves). These variations are also inherited, so that it appears as if a new form has developed. For this reason they were once regarded, even in Darwin's time, as striking proofs of the inheritance of acquired characteristics. Today we see that they provide nothing new, but only new combinations of what already existed. They are not changes in the germ plasm but merely new groupings of the genes, which are contained as potentialities in the germ plasm. If, for example, butterflies in the chrysalis stage, which is the sensitive period, are brought into the cold, then hairy specimens develop. An edelweiss, planted on low ground, puts on a different appearance. But all such modifications due to change of site or climatic variations, revert again as soon as the organism concerned returns to its native conditions. Dandelion plants, some of which are planted in the highlands and the others in the plains, develop quite differently. In the highlands they are much smaller and hairy. When transplanted again on to low ground, they exhibit their old form and size. Thus the evolutionary tendencies can be altered by external influences; but these are not really mutations, but merely re-groupings of heritable dispositions already given. The question is therefore far more sharply presented nowadays than ever before. Are there, besides the non-hereditary para-variations and the hereditary mixo-variations, genuine mutations, that is real alterations of the germ plasm? Is there inheritance, not merely of inborn, but of really acquired characteristics?

We can nowadays put this question to nature much more clearly, because we make a sharp distinction between the *soma* (body) of the single individual, which occurs in the development of a species, and the germinal pathway along which the genes are transmitted from one individual to its offspring, and so inherited from generation to generation. The *somata* of the individuals are only by-products of the germinal path. In the latter the stream of inheritance flows on down from the progenitors. This process of inheritance is relatively independent of the destiny of any given individual. The individual bodies are like the leaves, flowers, and fruits which grow every year out of the trunk and branches of a tree. If these leaves and flowers wither away in a year of drought, or are blasted by cold or torn off by children, that does nothing to alter the capacity of the tree-trunk to produce similar leaves and flowers next year. The tails of mice have been cut off, and the tails of their offspring likewise, and so on for many generations. It was thought that in this way ultimately mice would come into the world at least with shorter tails. But nothing of the sort happened. The germinal path which conveys the potentiality of long tails, was not thereby altered. For thousands of years circumcision was practised among oriental people. In vast regions of ancient China the feet of all women were deformed from their earliest childhood. No mutilation of this sort, practised continually among whole peoples, throughout countless generations, has ever become hereditary. These were always somatic variations only, without influence on the germ-path. We must therefore put the question as follows: Are there influences by which the germinal pathway itself undergoes an alteration, so that the process in which the germ-cell is reproduced by division changes its direction?

Even up to about twenty years ago the experts gave a very cautious answer to this question, and at the fifth International Congress on Genetics in Berlin in 1927, a mood of resignation still at first prevailed. Of the best-known experimental animal in modern genetics, the fruit- or banana-fly, *Drosophila melanogaster*, it was reported that more than twenty million individuals had been bred by geneticists in order to obtain only the small number of about four hundred mutants. The attempts to produce mutations in the Colorado beetle by some kind of external influence had failed. The situation seemed hopeless. In regard to the basic question of biology, which is of the most far-reaching importance for our whole conception of life, it seemed that for a long time to come we were faced with an "*ignoramus et ignorabimus.*" Bertalanffy in 1928 was still saying: "The principal and most crucial question for the problem of evolution, whether or not the genotype is changed, cannot be solved by experimental methods." Then a quite unexpected turn of events took place which suddenly altered the situation.

In the course of this fifth Congress on Genetics the American H. J. Müller reported on the results achieved by the Morgan School in experiments on animals and plants (*Drosophila*, the ichneumon fly, *habrobracon*, tobacco plants, maize, barley, etc.) by treating the eggs, larvae, and pupae with short-wave rays (X-rays and ultra-violet rays). In *Drosophila* at first 16·5 per cent of the offspring showed mutations. Hereditary abnormalities appeared in the structure of the wings, in the colour of the eyes, and in the pattern of the body. When the period of exposure to the rays was increased (from 12 to 48 minutes), the number of mutants (including lethal and sterile cases) rose to 76·8 per cent. It was possible to determine that as a result of this radiation, not only the chromosomes, those carriers or "vehicles" in which the genes lie ranked in line, but individual genes, which lie in an arithmetically definable locus of a known chromosome, were themselves altered. The free electrons produced by the X-rays seem to descend like a barrage directly on the substance of heredity itself. By increasing the dose of radiation, the mutations were correspondingly multiplied. Thus (from the point of view of quantum mechanics) the greater the number of particles contained in the barrage, the more mutations occur in the germ-cells they encounter. It was likewise demonstrated in the experiments of Goldschmidt, that on raising the temperature to between 35° and 37° C., for example, the pigment on the back or in the eyes of the test animal diminishes in proportion (mass stimulus effect). Since short-wave rays can not only be produced in the laboratory, but also occur freely in nature (β-rays, cosmic rays, etc.), Müller conjectured that these rays may also be the natural source of mutations. In fact, an increase of the mutation rate was also found in animals inhabiting a tunnel which passed through radioactive ore. Since then a multitude of experiments have been carried out on vegetable and animal cells, not only with short-wave rays but also with changes of temperature. On the basis of these new observations, W. Zimmermann,[3] in his comprehensive work on the inheritance of acquired characteristics, after examining all the objections, is able to answer the hotly debated question with a carefully weighed affirmative. The observations have shown, that "the rigid application of the dogma of constancy among hereditary factors," inferred from the Mendelian laws of inheritance, "has vastly overshot the mark and requires correction." "Do the factors of heredity change, and are they transmitted to the offspring in a changed state? . . . We can give a definitely affirmative answer to this fundamental question, although only a few years ago it was answered in the negative by leading geneticists. Notwithstanding the millions of transmissions without alteration we are faced today with the equally assured evidence of some thousands of instances of change in the hereditary factors – with the evidence of mutations." If, for example, we compare the fossilised remains of plants from earlier formations with the plants of today, it is seen that "the forerunners of the organisms of today were of quite a different kind, and we can only understand such a variation as a transformation of the inheritance." All these changes, however, must at some time have appeared as differences in the heredity of parents and offspring. "If at the end of the hologenetic series the inheritance is found to be different from that at the beginning, there must at least once have been offspring with a different inheritance from their parents." Many "micro-mutations," that is small variations in heredity, give rise in the long run to quite considerable differ-

[3] *Vererbung "erworbener Eigenschaften" und Auslese*, Jena 1938.

ences of inheritance. There are, therefore, not merely small variations within the limits of a species, but also transformations of the substance of heredity beyond the limits of the species itself. Erwin Bauer, who ranks as the leading expert on the problem of mutation, and who has carried out detailed experiments, especially in the culture of dandelions, observes, indeed, that: "We cannot yet determine where the seat of the mutation is to be found in the chromosome"; yet he ventures to say that, on the basis of all the observations, successive mutations of the genes are possible, by which differences among species and genera can in fact be bridged.

From all this it follows that mutation of the hereditary substance may be regarded today as established. Thus the seemingly insuperable obstacle in the way of the theory of evolution has been set aside. There is no longer any fundamental objection which can be raised against the fact of evolution.

Now we must also give serious consideration to the second question, which has aroused the fiercest controversy; namely the problem as to how evolution takes place – an issue that has revived once more on a higher level the old battle between mechanism and vitalism. If the higher species actually evolve from the lower, is this evolution of new species a product of aimless forces? Or must we explain it by postulating directing or purposeful factors, which guide the evolution according to a plan? W. Zimmermann's discussion of the objections against selectionism gives the impression that it is only the opponents of Darwinism who have drawn a negative philosophical conclusion from the theory of selection, by asserting that "it has claimed to resolve the purposeful in a mechanical, that is to say, non-theological fashion." But this negative conclusion has repeatedly been drawn, not only by the opponents, but also by distinguished representatives of the selection theory itself. Weismann, in his lectures on the theory of evolution, summarised the meaning of this doctrine schematically in these words: "Our time has solved the great riddle of how the purposeful can evolve without the co-operation of forces with an active purpose." It was utterly remote from the intention of Darwin himself, of course, to attempt any explanation of the evolution of purposeful structures. He assumed the existence of organisms, themselves endowed with a purposive structure, to be something manifestly given. But the theory of selection has aroused such a passionate battle about ultimate questions of *Weltanschauung* only because its most distinguished champions in Germany have in fact presented it as having succeeded in wholly eliminating all purposive factors from our picture of nature. Ernst Häckel, in his day, once hailed Darwin at a scientific congress as the Newton of the organic world. He believed that Darwin's principle of selection would have the same significance for the explanation of organic life in general as Newton's law of gravitation had once had for physics. In the period after Newton it was thought that the key to the mechanical explanation of all physical and chemical processes had been found, and that the entire world processes would in increasing measure be reduced to large, small, and very minute solar systems, in which the elements of mass would mutually attract each other according to the principle of gravitation. In the same way Weismann and Häckel believed that the principle of selection had delivered us from the burdensome assumption of forces working to a plan, and had enabled us to comprehend the unfolding of all organic life as the working out of a blindly constraining causality.

Have we really reached the goal thus envisaged by the first pioneers of Darwinism in Germany? In this context it cannot be our business to follow in detail the current debate between Neo-Lamarckism and the revival of selectionism. But the fundamental question must be put. Has modern selectionism succeeded in eliminating the purposive factors from the process of organic evolution?

Zimmermann summarises the substance of the doctrine of selection in its modern form as follows: Whereas, according to Lamarck, hereditary variations do not occur haphazardly and without direction, but prefer a particular direction, namely that conducing to the adaptation and improvement of the living conditions of the organism, the Darwinian doctrine of selection reckons with only five given factors: 1. The existence of random mutations; 2. the over-production of offspring; 3. a conditional competitive struggle among organisms; 4. unequal "fitness" of the organisms; 5. a "chance" for the fitter in this struggle to survive and so to produce more offspring (natural selection).

The crucial advance by which the new formulation goes

beyond Darwin, and also beyond Häckel, lies in the fact that the "variations," which in Darwin and Lamarck might be very diverse in origin, are replaced by the definite concept of "mutations." By means of this idea the entire outcome of the genetics founded by Mendel is incorporated into the *new theory of selection*. Mutation is a change of inheritance, as understood in genetics. It can be either a mutation of the gene, or a disturbance of the chromosome structure, or a regrouping of hereditary factors, or any other change of heredity.

This gives rise to a new situation with regard to the question with which Darwinism confronts our world view. For now the decisive process no longer takes place in public. The process which supplies the presupposition for the struggle for existence among organisms and the survival of the fittest, namely the development of mutations between which natural selection makes the choice, now occurs behind the scenes. For we cannot inspect the "steering mechanism" by which these inner changes come about. The decisive process takes place to a certain extent beyond our ken, namely in the sub-microscopic realm. We can, it is true, go on calculating the locus where a gene molecule is to be found within the chromosome. We even have some information as to which of the characteristics of the entire organism is contained potentially in a particular gene, but we cannot penetrate more deeply into this secret workshop of creation. We are therefore faced with an insoluble riddle. How does it come about that the germinal pathways, which carry on the inheritance from generation to generation, always give rise to forms inherently purposive and capable of life, and not, say, a mass of meaningless chance-productions, of which only a very few are at all fit to compete in the struggle for existence? This was in fact how Empedocles imagined it,[4] when that ancient pioneer of the radical idea of selection thought it out to its logical conclusion as early as the fourth century B.C. According to Empedocles, organisms are the result of the purposeless sport of the elements. At first single organs make their appearance, such as eyes without faces, arms without bodies, and so on. This leads to a disordered jumbling of bodies, until by a chance encounter of the elements at last a creature arises capable of life. In fact, we find nothing of the

[4] See J. Burnet, *Greek Philosophy: Thales to Plato*, London 1914.

sort even among the fossils; and even in the case of the mis-
creations which can be produced, for example, by strong irra-
diation or by over-heating of the genes in the embryonic stage
of *Drosophila*, such as creatures with lamentably crippled wing
appendages which are utterly useless, one has the impression
that there must still have been present in the particular gene,
humanly speaking, the will to a pair of wings, although this
will has been disturbed and hindered in the carrying out of its
plan by natural forces from outside. Why is it that in the extravagant over-production of offspring, which we find everywhere
in nature, there are no senseless combinations, doomed in
advance to die out? Why do we get beings which, though
admittedly more or less capable of life, are yet plainly inherent
purposeful wholes, shaped to a specific pattern, able to enter
into the arena as combatants in the great struggle of life and
death? The strongest objection which used to be raised against
Darwinism in its older form was indeed the fact of "co-adapta-
tion." What does this mean?

Gustav Wolff, in a book called *Beiträgen zur Kritik der
darwinischen Lehre* ("Contributions to the criticism of the
Darwinian teaching"), which in 1890 no publisher had yet
dared to print, remarks: "If any variation in an organism is to
have an advantage in the struggle for existence, it is not enough
for that purpose that there should be a change only in the form
of a single element, such as a life-cell; on the contrary, there
must always be numerous different parts of the organism which
so change together that their purposeful co-operation leads to
an advantageous result. The eye, for example, is part of the
pattern of an animal. How could it gradually have been bred
in by an accumulation of small variations in heredity? Eyes
are traced back from simple pigment spots; we then meet the
already more advanced flattened eye (of fishes), on which a
lens may further be imposed. But in a cuttlefish this lens is
produced from quite different tissues and is of quite a different
form from that of mammals, and this fact constitutes a difference of plan, the one being inexplicable as an evolutionary
consequence of the other. How could the delicate relations of
nerve and muscle, of stamen and pistil, have been built up
gradually by single stages? How can the wonderful system of
balance in the ear, or the minutely integrated unity of a gland,

with its interrelations to the whole organism, be explained by individual hereditary stages?"[5] In all such cases different organs must be simultaneously varied in different ways, if an effect advantageous to selective breeding is to emerge. Take, for example, the eye and the optic ganglia; an organ and the associated instinct for its use; the uterus and the egg; the male and female sex-organs; insects and flowers; the stunting of the female sex-organs in worker bees and the development of pouches on their legs. In all these cases the element of purpose is correlative.

The answer to this objection, put forward by W. Zimmermann in defence of the modern theory of selection, is very instructive. "This objection," he says, "dates in spirit from the time (before knowledge of the laws of heredity) when general changes in the laws of heredity were confused with phenotypic changes. Today this objection lapses into insignificance. For it is now quite clear to anyone at all familiar with genetics, that the change in an hereditary factor for one eye simultaneously occasions a corresponding change in the second eye. Normally all the organs of an individual which are similar, or homologous – the two eyes of a vertebrate, the hundreds of tentacles of a *Medusa*, the thousands of leaves on a tree – are influenced alike by a single factor of heredity. Thus, in general, such organs have been changed alike in the history of the race, when, for example, the bearer of a variant factor of heredity became dominant through selection."

This answer is plausible. But the matter we are anxious to understand is not really elucidated thereby. The mysterious fact that we wish to understand is surely this: When a new species evolves through mutation from a more primitive original form, for example, a *Drosophila*, a house-fly, a wasp, a bumble-bee, and so on, the individual parts always mutate in such a way that the mutations of all the individual organs correspond to each other, so that out of their harmonious co-operation, as from the harmony of many instruments in an orchestra, a living whole results. How is this possible? To this question the answer given is: Very simple; it is always one and the same factor of heredity which produces the organs corresponding to each other in every detail, and which changes them

[5] Heinrich Frieling, *Herkunft und Weg des Menschen*, Stuttgart 1949, p. 81.

in the same way. In other words, in the gene molecules from which a new species emerges, there must be a force at work which ensures that the mutations of the individual organs correspond with each other exactly. Since hitherto we have not been able to inspect the "steering mechanism" inside the gene molecules, even with the electron-microscope, this means that the riddle we are anxious to solve is likewise put away in the dark-room, in which the picture is being developed which afterwards confronts us in the complete mechanism. With our powers of observation we cannot penetrate any further into the heart of this process of growth. We can indeed confirm, but can no longer understand, how this great orchestra of mutually concordant processes of organic growth can come into being. Nor can we come a step nearer understanding this process by chemical or physical methods. For with all chemical and physical influence, whether by short-wave radiation, changes of temperature, or mechanical interference with the development of the germ-cells, such as the Spemann School[6] have undertaken with their transplantations, we can invariably make a start only when the process of growth within the germ-cell is already under way. We can disturb and hamper this mysterious process; we can even divert it and give it a new direction, as a signalman, by pulling a lever, switches a moving train from one line to another. But how this creative process itself comes about, striving purposefully with elemental force towards the realisation of a specific total form, is something we cannot make intelligible by any of these chemical and physical experiments. As before, we are left always with two possibilities. Either we accept this process of becoming as an incomprehensible, original datum, and renounce any further explanation; or we are faced, at this very central point, whence the co-operation of corresponding mutations is directed, with the fundamental law to which we have repeatedly been led in our consideration of the life process. As the whole of a melody is present before the individual notes from which it is composed, so here too we are faced with a totality which can no longer be broken into parts, and which guides the composition of the organism according to a definite plan.

How we are to account for this *tendency to totality* in terms of

[6] Hans Spemann, *Embryonic Development and Induction*, London 1938.

natural philosophy is, of course, a further question. In doing so we must naturally free ourselves completely, as we saw earlier, from the anthropomorphic conception which Lamarckism involved, as if there were seated somewhere in the organism a hidden man-like director guiding the interplay of forces, a "hobgoblin" at work within it. But even the Aristotelian concept of entelechy, which Hans Driesch has introduced in this context, is merely a name for the inexplicable factor here at work. If we wish to express this factor conceptually, in a manner at least partially free from objection, we must do as has been attempted in this book, and get beyond the whole three-dimensional, objective space, which alone is accessible to our observation, and penetrate to a different kind of space, in which the content of the world is arranged according to different structural laws. But however we fit the operation of unifying tendency into the total picture of our natural philosophy, the decisive point is this: Even the modern selectionists must concede that in the heart of the germ-cell, in the gene molecules, something happens which can no longer be explained by random processes, but is directed to the production of an end-form. Then, for the rest, we can acknowledge without reserve all that has been adduced as evidence of the tremendous significance of selection in the higher evolution of the organic world. In the extravagant over-production of offspring within the living world, and the competitive struggle thereby occasioned, the "better chance" given to the fittest to survive in the struggle for existence and to produce offspring, is indeed the sieve which automatically eliminates inferior types from among the wealth of non-directed mutations, and so helps to preserve the purity and improve the quality of the species. But this automatically-working apparatus, whereby the worthy survive and the remainder perish, can produce nothing living of itself. It can only serve to eliminate life unworthy of living; it can only polish and refine. It can, therefore, only come into force when an abundance of organisms have already appeared on the battlefield of life, which in themselves represent purposeful wholes.

Thus three conditions must always be simultaneously fulfilled, if the world of organic life is to arise and develop: 1. there must exist organic wholes, in which a force operates with the aim of creating and preserving specific forms of life; 2. these unitary forms must in the course of propagation undergo non-directed mutations; 3. among these last, natural selection must make a choice according to the Darwinian laws. Thus the tendency to wholeness, which aims at the end-form, is the foundation on which everything else is built, the indispensable basic condition, without which the other two conditions simply could not come into operation at all. If this is so, then the enterprise whose execution Weismann once described as the great task reserved for our time, the attempt "to explain the purposeful order without the aid of purposive forces," has ended in failure.

If we must everywhere take account of the directed tendency to wholeness as the first basic factor in the interpretation of the organic world, we ought not to regard it merely as a subsidiary factor which only appears sporadically at certain points, but as an omnipresent factor which belongs to the nature of reality. It must therefore be our primary assumption that this factor is at work, not merely in the composition of the individual organism from the heredity factors received from its progenitors, but also in the composition of the family tree, in which a multiplicity of whole species and genera emerges from a common primeval form. For there is surely a striking similarity between the evolution of a single creature from a germ-cell, and the development of a whole species from a primeval form. Karl Beurlen calls the higher structure of a species or genus a "phyletic form," or generic unity. Just as the individual in the womb appears first in the form of an embryo, then passes through the stages of youth and maturity, and finally a period of old age which ends in death, so also, according to Beurlen, the generic form is subject to youth, maturity, and age. Take, for example, the genus of the saurians, beginning small and humble with the cotylo-saurians, then entering on their triumphal march and exhausting all their inherent possibilities, but finally falling into the senescence of gigantism and "obesity," from which they perished in the Cretaceous Age. Similar changes were undergone by the genus of elephants and horses. If the evolution of the individual creatures is directed by a factor of wholeness, which is operative in the gene molecules of the individual, then it is to be assumed that the same tendency to wholeness is operative also in the development of genera and species. If, out of the common root of a primeval form (primeval plant, primeval animal, etc.) a widely-branching family tree of genera and species emerges, in which all the potentialities contained in the primeval type are exhausted, this mighty process, which stretches throughout millions of years, is invariably governed by the co-operation of the same three factors which we have encountered in the individual creature: 1. the organic tendency to wholeness, which aims at the creation and multiplication of a specific type; 2. the appearance of non-directed mutations, leading to variations; 3. the process of natural selection by breeding, which, like an automatic sieve, sifts out the ageing and less well-adapted, and so allows whole genera to die out and make way for younger and stronger genera. Only from this standpoint can we understand the fact that the family tree of organic life, as we saw above, constitutes not a chaos of aimless and confused developments, but a planned ascent, leading to an end and reaching a perfection which can no longer be surpassed.

CHAPTER 2

THE CREATION OF THE WORLD
ACCORDING TO THE BIBLE

1. *The Creation of the Universe*

IN the previous chapters we have given a review of cosmogony according to the views of modern science. This review has occupied a comparatively large space, and so we are able to make all the briefer our treatment of the Biblical doctrine of creation, to which we now come.[1] This begins precisely where natural science and its methods come to an end. For science can only explain the world of today from an element which was already present at the beginning. The Bible has something to say about the question how this primeval element arose, and its answer can be briefly summarised in one sentence which is also the title-heading of the first chapter of the Bible: "In the beginning God created the heavens and the earth."

"In the beginning," that means, according to the exegesis of the old Protestant dogmatist: *in principio illo, in quo tempus fluere coepit*: in that starting-point, in which time began to flow. The Bible thus reaches back to a primeval state in which there was as yet no time. Only God Himself could in the real sense of the word begin. All beginning within the world of polarity is at the same time always an ending of the period of time which stretches to the point at which we stand, and so always presupposes the pre-existence of time itself. Here we encounter a pre-temporal primeval state, in which God alone exists, when there is as yet no world. The clearest expression of this is in the following "prayer of Moses, the man of God":

[1] Special reference should be made to the valuable writings of Hans Engelland, *Am Anfang schuf Gott Himmel und Erde*, Berlin 1938; and Dietrich Bonhoeffer, *Schöpfung und Fall*, 3rd edn. Munich 1955; Eng. trans. *Creation and Fall*, London 1959.

Lord, thou hast been our dwelling place
   in all generations.
before the mountains were brought forth,
   or ever thou hadst formed the earth and the world,
from everlasting to everlasting
   thou art God.

(Ps. xc.1, 2.)

Here we stand face to face with the absolute being of God, which exists as yet outside the time-form, which is from ever-lasting to everlasting. Only because God has absolute being can we, who are contained in the time-form, trust in God and cleave to God in the midst of the restless surge of time by which we are borne away. Of this God, who exists in a supra-temporal and so in a supra-polar way, it is said in the first verse of the Bible: He created time and with it heaven and earth. Every-thing which lives and moves within the world of polarity has accordingly been placed there from out of the supra-polar world. What we mean by the word 'create" (*bara*, κτίζειν), a word which, as we shall see below, is reserved exclusively for God's creation, is thus best expressed if we define it as an im-plantation from the supra-polar space into the space of polarity, or to put it more simply, an implanting from eternity into time. The question thus arises, how does this implanting come about? The Bible answers that it does so through the Word. The Word of God is thus in this context a decision which is taken in the supra-polar world, and then put into execution in the world of polarity according to the text: "For he spoke, and it came to be; he commanded, and it stood forth" (Ps. xxxiii.9). In contrast to all the words that are spoken in the earthly world, the Word which is spoken in the supra-polar world is thus followed immediately by the execution of its content, because it meets with no resistance of any kind. There are also special cases where earthly speech takes the form of a decision which is at once translated into action. This is the case with military commands. Here we have the nearest approximation in our earthly sphere to the supra-polar Word of God. We see this in the story of the Centurion of Capernaum, who asks Christ to heal his slave who is sick to death, saying: "For I am a man under authority, with soldiers under me; and I say to one, 'Go,' and he goes, and to another, 'Come,' and he comes, and to my slave, 'Do this,' and he does it" (Mt. VIII.9). This command of an officer, which is not contradicted (except in the case of a mutiny), is here seen as the closest analogy to the almighty Word of God, although it is still within the limitations of the world of polarity and therefore is not absolutely irresistible. The Roman Centurion therefore says to Christ, whose divine authority he recognises: "but only say the word, and my servant will be healed." (Mt. VIII.8). The word, which is spoken of in Gen. 1.1, is thus a decision taken in the eternal world, which is put into effect in the temporal world without meeting the slightest resistance. It is this sovereign Word which is meant also in Jn. 1.1ff., where Gen. 1.1 is plainly referred to: "In the beginning was the Word, and the Word was with God, and the Word was God"; that is, as Bultmann explains: "God only exists in His revelation, and whoever encounters that revelation, really encounters God."[2] "He was in the beginning with God; all things were made through him, and without him was not anything made that was made." In these words it is made plain that all things in the world exist in a double relationship. On the one hand they are produced by other earthly events, and so exist in the context of polar causality; on the other hand they owe their existence at every moment to the almighty Word of God. Everything that happens in the world therefore, happens on the one hand within the space of polarity, in which all the causes and effects of events are contained; and on the other hand in the supra-polar space of God, where the eternal decisions are taken. It belongs to the nature of God that everything outside God exists at the same time through and for God. Our own existence thus always belongs intrinsically to God Himself. When we devote our life to God, we are only giving Him back what belongs to Him.

There can be no clash between the two relationships, in which all things exist as a result of being on the one hand a part of the earthly scheme of things, and on the other hand as being based on an eternal, divine decision. Therefore, as we shall see more plainly later, a people which from the earthly point of view exists in the context of the family tree of humanity, can from the standpoint of eternity be described as the creation of

[2] R. Bultmann, *Das Evangelium des Johannes*, 11th edn. Göttingen 1950, p. 18.

God (Is. XLIII.1). We shall have to return to this double relationship, in which all things in the world exist, in a later connexion.
In the creation of God there thus lies a sovereign act of power
which meets with no resistance. Therefore God, and with Him
all the decisions which He takes, exist altogether beyond the
created world. His creation is a creation out of nothing (*creatio
ex nihilo pure negativo*). Here lies the profound contradiction
between the divine creation of which the Bible and all the
creation mythologies which existed in the ancient world tell us.
This is shown by a comparison with the highest creation myth
of the ancient world, which was read at the opening of every
New Year festival in Babylon as part of the liturgy. There the
creation is a battle which Marduk, the god of the city of
Babylon, wages successfully against the monster of chaos,
Tiamat. In the course of this battle the latter is overthrown.
The world is composed of the fragments of his carcase. The
Biblical belief in creation as found in the Old Testament is in
radical contrast even to the highest creation myth produced by
the ancient world, because it speaks of a creation which is
utterly incompatible with the pre-existence of any kind of
material or with the overthrow of any kind of chaotic resistance.

The Biblical idea of creation is just as incompatible with any
kind of emanation, in which the world issues from God as a
stream from its source, so that Rainer Maria Rilke, for example,
can address God as follows:

> With tremulous hands we're trying to upheave you,
>   one speck on another we cast.
> Who, though, can ever achieve you,
>   Minster vast?[3]

2. *The Creation of Man*

In Chapter 1, section 5 we made clear how, according to the
discoveries of modern palaeontology, the great revolution
came about which was to change the face of the whole earth.
We saw how there appeared on the stage that unique being,
who had in him those qualities of leadership which fitted him
for world dominion. Even if we consider this turning-point of
the world in which our own destiny is involved with the detach-

[3] Rainer Maria Rilke, *Selected Works*, VOL. II, trans. J. E. Leishmann, London
1960, p. 33.

ment of a spectator, as the natural scientist alone can do; if, that is to say, we ignore the ultimate background of our personal existence, it is clear that this last step in the evolution of the animal world which took place when Man was born, forms a much more profound transition than all the previous stages of progress, for example the step from vegetable to animal, or from single-celled, primitive animals to the vertebrates, and finally to the mammals. For with the birth of Man something entirely new appears, which can no longer be regarded as simply a development or perfection of any animal function. This new thing is *technical intelligence,* for which the theft of fire and the blazing torch have remained the shining symbols for all ages. This is the mysterious ability to control the powers of nature by deliberate reflexion and to use them for our service. The hearth with its charred objects lying among the remains of primitive human skulls, found in the excavations in loess deposits in the neighbourhood of Peking in North China, is the only sure evidence for the scientist that the birth of Man has actually taken place. Animals too use the substances found in their environment as building-material for their homes: they may make progress in using this material. The honey bee's comb, for example, is better adapted for its purpose and technically more perfect than the simpler honeycomb of the bumble-bee. But these advances in the control of material in the animal world obviously came about in an entirely different way from the technical inventions of Man. They arise not from conscious reflexion and calculated planning on the basis of accumulated experience, but by means of so-called instinct, which gropes its way forward in the dark like a blind man who, without seeing, finds his way through the guidance of a sure sense of locality and a highly developed sense of touch. Instinct and conscious reflexion certainly differ from one another in their operation. Where instinct prevails, there arises a movement which progresses only slowly and gradually, and which may stand still for thousands of years at one stage. There are many species of animal whose way of life has hardly changed since the Cambrian Age. Their evolution seems to have come to a standstill. On the other hand when reflexion has once begun, a process is unleashed which proceeds relentlessly and can never rest. For according to Kierkegaard, "the endlessness of reflexion" belongs to the essence of consciousness. Conscious thinking cannot call a halt at any conclusion at which it has arrived. It must go on asking questions persistently. Scientific research must dig deeper and deeper and penetrate more and more to the causes and secret foundations of reality. The spirit of technical invention cannot rest content with any invention, but must always be searching for new paths and trying out new methods, in order to solve the technical problem more quickly and more easily than before. Thus once primitive man's acquisition of fire has illuminated the technical intelligence, a decisive turning-point in the history of life has occurred. The still stream of biological evolution changes all at once into a rushing torrent. From the time of the later Diluvial Age onwards there is no longer any halting of technical progress. One invention succeeds another. In quick succession the crudely-worked stone tools of the earlier Stone Age are replaced by better and more skilful artefacts. Towards the end of the Palaeolithic Age, in the Aurignacian period, the first pottery appears. In the later Stone Age pile-dwellings arise on the shores of the lakes. Soon afterwards weaving looms follow. Already the first wheels are in motion. Carts are mounted on wheels. The first ships are built and fitted with rudders.

These results show that with the appearance of technical intelligence something entirely new, something that never before existed, did indeed come into operation. It is fundamentally different from all the other factors which hitherto propelled the evolution of life in the world. Everything else which distinguishes Man physically from the animals nearest akin to him, such as his erect gait, greater cranial capacity, etc., can be regarded as continuous developments of qualities which are already present at the earlier stages of the family tree of the primates. It is quite different with the appearance of the creative, technical talent for invention, in a creature which has otherwise grown directly out of the animal context. This is indeed the epoch-making event, which suddenly sets in motion a process destined in a short time to change the face of the earth entirely. How this ability arose and was all of a sudden present is quite inexplicable. It bursts forth with creative power from hidden depths, as a strong spring gushes forth, destined to become a river which overflows everything. We thus see that the emergence of technical intelligence, with which the birth of Man begins, is from the scientific point of view quite inexplicable. The rise of this capacity, which introduces a new epoch in the history of the world, is just as great a miracle as the rise of organic life from the elements of inorganic nature.

Have we thus stumbled upon a characteristic which gives Man an absolute and undeniable superiority over the animals, and so gives him a unique place in the whole created world? Yes and No. For on the one hand he lacks the strength which would give him superiority over the strong animals, and also the specialisation of the limbs which would adapt him to all the conditions and perils of his environment. He is thus a creature helpless against all eventualities. But on the other hand, by means of his talent for invention he can meet successfully every attack or challenge. He can produce for himself the environment which he requires. His very lack of specialisation is the natural basis for every technical activity. He produces the tools with which he works; and they are his limbs, which he brings forth in manifold forms. In this way he is far superior to every created animal, however differentiated or strong its limbs. For an instinctive, specialised adaptation such as many animals possess is just like physical adaptation, in having disadvantages as well as advantages; namely, that other senses or limbs are developed much more feebly or subnormally. There is no question of this with Man. His technical ability is operative in every direction, and can be strengthened on every side. Thus the special strength of Man consists in this lack of specialisation.

Moreover a bodily specialisation is there for all time and remains permanently, with its disadvantages as well as its advantages. But when, as a result of change of climate or migration to other lands, the specialisations lose their function or even become disadvantages, the decline of the species is inevitable. Man, by reason of his lack of physical specialisation, combined with his gift of reason, is immune from this danger.

When we follow the evolution of mankind since the rise of technology, the pessimistic thought may come to our mind that technical intelligence has indeed been on the one side a blessing to mankind, and has contributed enormously to the ease and progress of his life; but that on the other side, technology has been the curse of the human race. For this is the tragedy of humanity, that the same technical achievements which should serve to promote and adorn life, have at the same time supplied the most fearful weapons to destroy all life upon the earth. They have unleashed a war of mutual destruction between nations and races, compared with which the struggle between plant stocks and animal kingdoms appear to us as harmless feuds. The creative inventiveness in the mind of Man is thus only another instrument in the struggle for existence waged by Man as well as by the beasts against all the powers which threaten him.

Is there anything which gives Man a unique place in the whole natural world, and exalts him in an absolute sense above the animals? No absolute contrast between Man and beast can be seen so long as our consideration is confined to the objective field, in which there can indeed only be differences of degree. We have already come across one difference earlier, in the section on principles in Volume IV of this work,[1] a difference which cannot be made at all evident in the objective field, yet by which certain features and realities are marked out from their whole environment. This is the difference which is expressed by the personal pronoun "mine." "My home," "my age," "my body," objectively considered, are not in any way distinguishable from other places, times, and physical forms. Seen from the neutral standpoint of natural science all places and times are of equal importance. For the definition of causal connexions and causal laws, with which science is concerned, it is quite immaterial whether the events in which these laws and connexions can be demonstrated are happening at this moment before my eyes, or whether they took place millions of years ago. But the chain of destiny which binds me inescapably to this my place and this my time constitutes a distinction between the here and now and all other places and times which is of tremendous importance. Then the section of that book on principles led us a stage further, namely to the question of the origin of this inescapable and non-transferable destiny. We saw that, if I am compelled on spiritual grounds to reject the titanic delusion that I have determined myself,

[1] *Der christliche Gottesglaube und die Naturwissenschaft*, Hamburg 1949; Eng. edn. *Christian Faith and Natural Science*, trans. N. H. Smith, London 1953.

there is nothing left but the belief that I have been set in this place without my aid by the Eternal Thou in whose presence all beings live, by the one Subject that can never become an object. That distinction, which is not at all evident on the objective plane, and which I can only express by the indefinable word "mine," is endowed with an absolute significance and an eternal meaning through this fact. This point in space and time is the place which God has appointed for me by His eternal decree. This moment is the point where eternity and time make contact with each other, as the tangent that extends to infinity makes contact at one point with the circle that is enclosed within itself. The infinite difference by which this point is distinguished from its environment cannot be made evident by any objective distinguishing mark. Externally considered, as seen from the standpoint of an observer, this distinction seems utterly arbitrary. It seems as if the Now might just as well lie at some other point of time. Only when I see the event from the inside, and so am myself by my own existence restricted to this moment, do I experience the ineluctable necessity with which the moment has me in its power.

The fixation of the Ego-point, which was the subject of more detailed discussion in the section on principles, is primarily a first and particularly important example of the fact that within the reality to which we belong, distinctions occur which are not evident in the sphere of objective observation, and are only intelligible to us because, along with the whole of reality, we live simultaneously in another sphere, the non-observational sphere. If this occurs in this one case, we must be prepared to find other cases in which the same kind of distinctions occur.

This thought brings us to the distinction which, according to the Biblical view, exalts Man above the whole animal world. Darwinism and discovery of the first fossil remains of transitional forms between the man-like primates and *homo sapiens* produced at the time a great uneasiness in Christian circles, because it was thought that Man could only occupy the place which the Bible ascribes to him in the divine plan of the world, if he proceeded directly from the creative hand of God as a new creation, without any link with the plants and the other animals. But as soon as it was proved that Man has grown out of the stock of other forms of life in the world, he is no longer the central creature, standing in the centre of creation. His patent of nobility is lost, the dignity which belongs to Man according to the Scriptures is destroyed. In consequence the central importance which, according to the Gospel of salvation, is given to Man in the divine purpose for the world vanishes. There is no longer any sense in saying that a human soul is of more value than the whole world.

Here two things are obviously inseparably linked together: first the genealogical descent of Man, and secondly the value of Man in the sight of God, the place which he occupies in the divine plan of the world. Before we approach any of the particular pronouncements which the Bible makes about Man, we must therefore first of all put the fundamental question, on the solution of which the answer to all other questions depends. What is the relation, according to the Biblical view, of these two things to each other, the genealogical origin of a creature, and the value of this creature in the sight of God? Is the significance of a member of the created world in the eyes of God in any way conditioned or determined by the history of its ancestors?

To this question of principle the New Testament gives its answer in no uncertain terms. For the men who played a prominent part at the beginning of the New Testament era repeatedly found it necessary to think out their basic attitude to this question. In New Testament Christianity, indeed, faith in God burst the national limits of the religion of ancient Israel with elemental force. "The new wine bursts the old skins," as Christ once said (Mk. 11.22). The Gospel of the Kingdom of God was brought to all nations. The new thing which here emerged from the depths inevitably came into fierce conflict with the ancient religious privileges of the Jewish people, and with their claim on the basis of their ancestry to be the heirs of the promises given by God to their forefathers. In the controversy between the new movement and the Jews, on whose territory it had first grown up, it became a burning question, whether in relation to God there are any privileges at all which could be based on ancestry. The new movement could only break down the national barriers in which it was at first confined, and win free scope for its triumphal progress throughout the world, if it had achieved a decisive, positive answer to this question.

The forerunner of Jesus, John the Baptist, already in his preaching of repentance in the wilderness at the river Jordan found a truly classical formulation for the New Testament answer to the genealogical claim of the Jews, when he says to them: "Do not begin to say to yourselves, 'We have Abraham as our father'; for I tell you, God is able from these stones to raise up children to Abraham" (Lk. III.8). In other words, because God is the almighty Creator and Lord of all the world, all privileges which a creature presumes to claim on the basis of its descent from other creatures are reduced to nothing in His presence. What God will make of a creature depends entirely on His sovereign decree. This decree is altogether independent of the origin of the creature within the context of earthly causality. God did not even need to take the creatures which He wished to use for His plan out of the organic world. He could even descend to the mineral kingdom and "raise up children" "from these stones," that is from inorganic material. He could take something out of the inanimate world and exalt it directly to Himself. How much more could He receive into the family of God every living creature, all of whose beings are derived from the vegetable kingdom or from the animal world or from primitive human conditions?

This idea, with which John the Baptist radically demolished every claim to racial superiority, every attempt to derive a religious privilege from the "certificate of pure ancestry" was adopted and developed by Paul. For Paul was, as Houston Stewart Chamberlain rightly recognised,[2] the real pioneer of the universal Christian movement and the liberator of the Gospel from the fetters of Jewish nationalism. For this reason the apostle was persecuted with fanatical hatred by his Jewish kinsmen. Just as Luther was able to begin at the most central point in his work of emancipation as a Reformer, because he himself had all his roots in the medieval Church, so Paul, just because he was a man educated in the Rabbinic school, was

[2] Houston Stewart Chamberlain, *The Foundations of the Nineteenth Century*, London 1907, of which twenty-three German editions were published before 1938. The reference is to the Nuremberg racial laws which made a certificate of Aryan descent a condition of marriage in National Socialist Germany.

peculiarly fitted to get to grips with the Jewish claim, even from the purely theological standpoint in the controversy with the Old Testament. His starting-point was from the deepest sense of the divine calling of Israel to be the People of the Covenant. This calling, as Paul explains in Rom. ix.6ff., came about in this way, that God made a selective separation within the descendants of Abraham. "For not all who are (genealogically) descended from Israel belong to Israel, and not all are children of Abraham because they are his descendants"; rather "through Isaac shall your descendants be named." This means: not the children of the flesh (who in the fleshly sense are descendants of Abraham, that is children of God), but the children of the promise are reckoned as descendants. The same principle, according to which Isaac was selected as bearer of the promise, is shown in the later generation in the choice of Jacob. To Rebecca it was said: "The elder will serve the younger." "Though they were not yet born," Esau, who from the genealogical point of view had the rights of the elder and could claim superiority, was placed behind his younger brother by a sovereign decree of God, "in order that God's purpose of election might continue" (ἵνα ἡ κατ' ἐκλογὴν πρόθεσις τοῦ θεοῦ μένῃ, Rom. ix.11).

The Biblical history of salvation thus keeps always clearly in view, in the first place, the biological causal connexion and the hereditary links by which the natural relations of descent come about. But although the natural process of growth is not in any way affected thereby, nor its fundamental significance diminished, there appears along with the human succession of generations which proceed from each other according to biological laws, a distinction which is still not evident to objective observation, because it comes from another dimension. This distinction arises from a sovereign act of God.

The New Testament introduces special words for the invisible distinction which is here defined. The very terminology is designed to contrast this distinction, which comes from eternity, with all superiorities which have arisen on the visible plane. What takes place on the visible plane is a becoming (γίγνεσθαι), a process, in which something issues according to the flesh from a seed (ἐκ σπέρματος κατα σάρκα). In contrast to this, the sovereign act of God is a supra-temporal "designation" (ὁρίζειν, Rom. 1.4) or predestination (προορίζειν), an eternal calling (καλεῖν), a divine choice (ἐκλογή). Even in Christ Himself the two spheres from which He is simultaneously descended are clearly contrasted with each other. "Who was descended from David according to the flesh, and *designated* Son of God in power according to the Spirit of holiness" (Rom. 1.3f.).

When we read such New Testament statements, we ask in astonishment: How can one and the same reality have a double origin? One and the same stream surely cannot be traced back to two sources, one of which rises high in the mountains, the other down in the valley. These two opposite derivations of one and the same thing seem to be irreconcilable.

Yet this double origin of the same reality at once becomes intelligible if there are two areas in which we, along with the whole of reality, exist simultaneously. We can see a certain object, for example the pyramid of Cheops, in two-dimensional plane space, if we fly over it in an aeroplane at a great height and photograph it from above. Then we see the lines of the pyramid as they appear in a two-dimensional plane. But the same structure looks plastic and solid as soon as we begin to realise that we and everything we see above and below us, exist in three-dimensional physical space. In this transition a distinction comes to light which had not been evident in the flat view, namely the contrast between height and depth. It becomes plain to us that the top of the pyramid lies higher, and the base of the pyramid lies lower. I can only perceive this distinction when I myself with my whole existence am transported into physical space, so that my whole picture of the world is no longer flat, but has acquired depth. This is only an elementary example from the world of objects, by which we can illustrate, in so far as these things can be illustrated at all, what must take place when it becomes clear to us that the objective picture of things and events which we obtain from the causal, scientific explanation of the world, is the view which arises within the limits of a certain space. But at the same time we exist in another space which transcends the senses, a space which has a different structure. This is shown by the fact that distinctions appear in reality which cannot be evident to the objective view. As soon as we become aware of our own non-objective existence, and no longer assiduously abstract from it, as must be done in scientific investigation, then the reality of this distinction impresses us with the same elemental force as inevitably impresses us in the objective view with the distinctions between greatness and smallness, length and shortness of a line, strength and weakness of an electric current.

This explains the fact which is constantly referred to in the Bible. When it becomes clear to me that the place in the world to which I am bound by my destiny possesses the invisible accent of eternity which God has laid upon it, my mind is at once open to the God-ordained contrast between election and non-election, chosen of God and not chosen. For the sake of illustration let us compare the contrast between objective and non-objective space with the relation between two-dimensional area and three-dimensional physical space. Then we can say that the causal connexion in which all events exist for the scientific observer belongs to the surface view, in which the dimension of depth is ignored. To the causality of the surface view belongs also the whole explanation of racial descent, the biological process of becoming, by which the genera and species have grown out of a single, uniform root. When we become aware of the aspect of depth, and with it of the invisible space in which all things exist simultaneously, we know that all events do not merely exist in the superficial, causal relation, but that they have a second origin besides this. They are likewise determined anew every moment out of the depth. They live by the breath of God and are sustained by God.

To this creation out of the depth which sustains all things belong also the divine acts of election and selection, which cannot be explained by superficial causal connexion. Already in the Old Testament, and still more in the New, repeated examples are given to show how God in His calling is independent of all distinctions of size, which play so great a part in the visible world, and how sovereign is His disregard of all worldly distinctions of rank and dignity. The fact that Israel was chosen as the instrument for a special religious mission does not depend, according to the Old Testament, on any racial superiority or any biological advantage. On the contrary it is said in Deut. VII.7ff.: "It was not because you were more in number than any other people that the Lord set His love upon you and chose you, for you were the fewest of all peoples [or otherwise translated "the least"]; but it is because the Lord loves you." In the election of David as king, God, proclaiming His will through Samuel, chose expressly the youngest of all the seven sons of Jesse, the one whom his father had not presented to the prophet because in his opinion he did not come into consideration at all (1 Sam. xvi.9ff.). In the New Testament too, the Apostles emphasise again and again how independent of all earthly advantages is the divine choice. Paul writes to the Corinthians: "For consider your call, brethren; not many of you were wise according to worldly standards, not many were powerful, not many were of noble birth; but God chose what is foolish in the world to shame the wise, God chose what is weak in the world to shame the strong, God chose what is low and despised in the world, even things that are not, to bring to nothing the things that are, so that no human being might boast in the presence of God" (1 Cor. 1.26ff.).

Let us make clear the principle that runs through all these passages.

1. The whole creation – Man, animals, plants, inorganic nature ($\varkappa\tau\acute{\iota}\sigma\iota\varsigma$) – forms one consistent unity in the sight of God. It is "creature." The creature is subject to the basic law of growth and decay. God is one "who alone hath immortality." In the pessimistic chapters of Ecclesiastes we read the words of the Preacher, Solomon, as was already said above: "For the fate of the sons of men and the fate of beasts is the same; as one dies, so dies the other. They all have the same breath, and man has no advantage over the beasts; for all is vanity. All go to one place; all are from the dust, and all turn to dust again" (Ecc. iii.19ff.).

> Man cannot abide in his pomp,
> he is like the beasts that perish.
>   (Ps. xlix.12, 20.)

One result of this is that in the Old Testament, in contrast to the aristocratic contempt for animals in the Greek world, there is a brotherly solidarity between man and the animals. The Old Testament legislation, in determining the punishment of physical injuries, places the beasts under the same responsibility and under the same penal code as human beings.

A human being is punished according to the rule of retaliation:
"An eye for an eye, a tooth for a tooth." And the same rule
applies to the bull which gores a man or woman: "When an
ox gores a man or woman to death, the ox shall be stoned"
(Ex. xxi.28). In the national repentance which the King of
Nineveh imposed on the whole city in order to avert the divine
wrath from the guilty people even at the last moment, the
beasts had to make repentance equally with the human beings:
"Let neither man nor beast, herd nor flock, taste anything;
let them not feed, or drink water, but let man and beast be
covered with sackcloth, and let them cry mightily to God; yea,
let everyone turn from his evil way" (Jon. iii.7f.).

It is not only in guilt and repentance that the animal world
shares. The whole creation is also included in the hope and
salvation of the perfecting of the world. This idea is, of course,
fully expressed only in the future expectation of the New
Testament Church, as in the words of Romans: "Because the
creation itself will be set free from its bondage to decay and
obtain the glorious liberty of the children of God. . . . We know
that the whole creation has been groaning in travail together
until now" (Rom. viii.21, 22). But already in the prophecy of
the Old Testament the animal world too has been embraced
in the kingdom of peace which is expected at the end of the
present world:

The wolf shall dwell with the lamb,
  and the leopard shall lie down with the kid,
  and the wolf and the lion and the fatling together,
  and a little child shall lead them.
The cow and the bear shall feed;
  their young shall lie down together;
  and the lion shall eat straw like the ox.
The sucking child shall play over the hole of the asp,
  and the weaned child shall put his hand on the adder's den.
                                              (Is. xi.6–8)

Thus already in the Old Testament the whole creation, in
spite of all the distinctions of its genera and species, forms one
family, self-contained and inwardly connected.

2. This closely-knit unity of the created world, with its
distinctions which are only relative, stands in contrast to God,

who is the only absolute. In all extra-Biblical religions, even in the higher religions of the ancient world empires of the Orient, not only the subordinate gods, but even the one supreme—god, in whom the pantheon of gods is comprehended as in a single apex, is involved in the process of becoming and in the causal connexions of the objective world. In the beginning of the Babylonian creation epic *Enuma elis* there is a time "when the gods did not exist, no one named them with names, fates were not determined by them." Then comes the event of the theogony, the birth of the gods. "Then were the gods in their midst created." In the contrast to this whole view of the contemporary oriental world the birth of the one God, who is over all, is utterly inconceivable for the Old Testament. "It knows no time when Jahwe may not have existed."[3] Of Him it is true: "I am the first, and I am the last, the same at all times" (Is. XLI.4).[4]

Here we see that the one God is from the beginning and beyond the whole system of causal connexion, outside the whole chain of causes and effects. He is not a link in the chain of causes, nor even the first link, the prime cause or the *primum movens*, but exists beyond all things. For this reason it becomes necessary in the Old Testament to introduce at this point an entirely new category, which was not as yet available for extra-Biblical thought, and which was lacking even in the contemporary Babylonian cult-religion. This is the category of created-ness in the special Biblical sense of the word. While within the objective plane there are always factors at work which have a limited field of operation in space and time, and are either in co-operation or in competition with other temporal factors so that they can only express themselves in conflict with them, here we have an authority which issues from a point beyond time and space, that is, from an omnipresent power. This authority cannot therefore be in competition with any factor operating in the objective world. For the one who is here at work sets aside as powerless the whole system of cause and effect, although the system goes on working without interference in its own sphere.

[3] W. Eichrodt, *Theologie des Alten Testaments*, VOL. II, Leipzig 1935, p. 48.
[4] So the author's translation. R.S.V. reads: "I, the Lord, the first, and the last; I am he."

To illustrate the fact that this struggle with conflicting forces or resistant factors is excluded in advance for this divine authority, the latter is constantly compared in the Bible with the command of an absolute monarch, whose word is law and cannot be contradicted. As soon as the command is uttered, it is instantly fulfilled. Without difficulty and without effort the thought is translated into action. "For he spoke and it came to be; he commanded, and it stood forth" (Ps. xxxiii.9). This utterly invincible authority comes from the sphere of the eternal and omnipresent world and enters with a direct impact into the sphere of temporal events. The Bible uses the word *bara* for this invincible authority of God, with which are contrasted all human achievement and all the effects produced by natural powers. To this category belongs above all the primeval act of choice and election, by which distinctions were ordained within the created world, which are independent of the objective process of becoming.

Now that we have made plain in principle the new category of absolute authority, we can make it the starting-point for our approach to the special question which led us to all these considerations. From the standpoint of the Bible, what is the basis for the superiority of Man over the rest of the created world? In the earlier Jahwistic account of the creation, which we find in Gen. ii.5ff., Man is from the first in the centre of the creation story. God formed Man: "Then the Lord God formed man of dust from the ground, and breathed into his nostrils the breath of life; and man became a living being" (Gen. ii.7). Here what is said in the first place about Man and his existence is exactly the same as what applies to all other animals. The same term is employed as is applied in the same way to birds, cattle, and wild beasts in the story of Noah (Gen. ix.10). Every animal is also *nephesh chajia*. What does this mean? All beings are physical bodies which come from the earth. But now they have received something which, as long as they possess it, exalts them above the dead matter of the earth. As soon as it is taken away from them again they sink, as if dragged down by the law of gravity, back into the inorganic primeval state above which they have for a short time been exalted. This gift, which raised them above the dead matter of the earth, is "the breath of God." "When thou sendest forth thy spirit they are created. . . . When thou

takest away their breath, they die, and return to their dust"
(Ps. CIV.29f.).

This is the sense in which we must understand what is said
of Man in the Jahwistic creation story: "God blew the breath
of life into his nostrils." It is not until the later account of
creation, which comes from a priestly narrator (Gen. I.Iff.),
that not merely Man, but the whole animate world in its
marvellous variety, comes into the field of vision. It appears
as an architectonic structure, rising higher and higher step by
step. First come the plants, then the water-creatures and birds,
then the land animals, and then on the highest step stands
Man.

If we ask how all these forms of life came into being, as they
are introduced to us here in all their variety, there are only two
things which are plain. First, all these living creatures did not,
so to speak, fall to earth from heaven like meteors from a
higher region plunging into this world, but they sprang from
this earth, and were formed from the material which it contains.
The plants arise when the earth causes young grass to sprout
or come up (Gen. I.IIf.). The sea-creatures, when the water
"brings forth swarms of living creatures" (1.20). The land
animals arise when it is said: "Let the earth bring forth living
creatures according to their kinds" (1.24). Of Man indeed it is
only in the earlier Jahwistic account that it is expressly said
that he is of the dust of the ground, and so, as is said later, he
"is earth," "out of the ground" (Gen. II.7, 19). But there is no
doubt that the priestly narrator too might have repeated this
statement from the earlier account without hesitation.

The second thing which is made plain to us is this. While
the living creatures have thus grown out of the earth, the origin
of all these creatures simultaneously comes under the new
Biblical category, which is expressed in the word *bara*. They
were all brought forth, not, as in the Babylonian creation myth,
by demonic forces in conflict with a chaotic primeval matter.
They were created. They were thus called out of nothingness,
without conflict, and without effort, by the absolute, invincible
decree of an omnipresent power having unlimited control over
the world.

In the whole Bible, one and the same reality is seen simultaneously from two different apsects, without the one disturb-

ing or abrogating the other. The fruits of the earth grow by a slow, natural process of development out of the ground. "The earth produces of *itself*, first the blade, then the ear, then the full grain in the ear. But when it [the earth] has brought forth the fruit, he [Man] puts in the sickle, because the harvest is come" (Mk. IV.28f.).[5] Regarded from the other side, all the fruits of the earth are "foods which God created" (1 Tim. IV.3).

This double way of regarding things, which is here applied to the world of plants, applies also to animals and human beings. In great detail the first books of the Pentateuch describe the long, natural process of evolution by which the people of Israel came into existence. The grandson of the racial ancestor, Abraham, had twelve sons, each of whom had numerous descendants who, after about 430 years, each came to form a whole tribe. Out of the tribes which thus arose the nation of Israel was later composed. Yet the same tribal history, which is here unfolded as a long process of growth from family to clan and from clan to nation, is seen in the light of prophetic vision as a single, creative act of God, by whom this people is brought from eternity into time. Thus we read in Is. XLIII.1: "But now thus says the Lord, he who created you, O Jacob, he who formed you, O Israel: 'Fear not for I have redeemed you, I have called you by name, you are mine.'"[6] In the same sense the Psalmist in Ps. CII.18 can as he prays look forward to the coming generations who will grow up in the course of history, and say: "Let this be recorded for a generation to come, so that a people that will be *created* may praise the Lord."[7] One and the same event is once more seen from the one side as a process of growth in the course of time, and from the other side is regarded as an act of creation.

And for this reason the acts of creation which the book of Genesis relates by no means exclude the view of biology that the new stage, which is attained with every new day of creation, had grown out of the lower stage by organic, progressive evolution. The priestly narrator wishes only to emphasise that it is

[5] So the author's translation. R.S.V. reads: "But when the grain is ripe, at once he puts in the sickle, because the harvest has come."

[6] So R.S.V. Author's translation has: "I call you by name." Friedrich von Huene rightly alludes to this significant passage in his essay *Die Erschaffung des Menschen nach Bibel und Naturwissenschaft*, 1941, p. 16.

[7] So the author's translation. R.S.V. reads: "a people yet unborn."

always the sovereign word of God's power which is the signal for "the earth" to "bring forth" the new kind of living creature.

Assuming these facts, in what then does the unique place which is occupied by Man within the created world consist, according to the Bible? It cannot be based on the ground that only Man was called to life by a new divine act of creation, while the animals came out of the water or the earth. For it is true also of other creatures, of stars, plants, birds, fish, mammals, every time a new word of power is spoken by God to call them into life. On the other hand, this divine order does not preclude the fact that these ascending stages of organic evolution can be regarded from the other side as proceding from the bosom of the earth.

What then is the basis of the claim that with Man it is not merely a higher stage of organic life that begins, but that here there appears a being exalted above all the rest of creation? The priestly document answers the question with the profound description of the creation of Man. God speaks first to the heavenly beings round about Him (the Elohim): "Let us make man in our image, after our likeness." Then comes the sentence which, in the poetic style of Hebrew parallelism, repeats the same thought in a double form. "So God created man in his own image, in the image of God he created him." This sentence has been interpreted by some in the sense of the Babylonian mythology, and they have taken the view that the image of God could only consist in the fact that the human body was similar to the form in which God appeared on earth in the theophanies. But Eichrodt rightly makes the objection that this interpretation is in absolute contradiction to the basic view of the priestly narrator, for whom God is an absolute, transcendental being, who cannot appear at all in any visible form. If, according to the second commandment, it is strictly forbidden as heathen idolatry to represent God in any image, this is inconsistent with the idea that every man who walks on the earth is such a representation of God. If the image of God does not refer to the bodily form, the idea might occur to one that some mental superiority was meant, which exalted Man above the beast, such as Man's technical intelligence, or his reason and freedom of will. But this would surely have been indicated in some way by the Biblical narrator. Instead he says only that

Man's creation in the image of God has the necessary consequence of His dominion over all creation. If we wish to penetrate to the true understanding of what is said in Gen. 1.26ff.
about the creation of Man, we must here set aside our own
ideas entirely, and look around for a passage in the Old Testament which sheds light on the original meaning of that sentence
in the priestly creation story. We find such a passage in Ps.
VIII.3–8. The Psalmist as he prays has a vision of a man standing in all his creaturely humility and insignificance in the immensity of the cosmos. "When I look at thy heavens, the work
of thy fingers, what is man?" But now it is as if an absolute ruler
by an incomprehensible act of grace takes a child of humble
origin right out of the street into his own palace, and has him
brought up among the royal princes at court, because he has
selected him for a high position. "What is man," it says, "that
thou art mindful of him, and the son of man that thou dost
care for him?" He makes man "little less than the divine
beings" (Elohim) who are in the divine presence, and "crowns
him with glory and honour." God thus takes this creature whom
He has exalted to Himself, and at the same time clothes him
with princely robes and invests him with royal honours. And
then it goes on: "Thou hast given him dominion over the works
of thy hands; thou hast put all things under his feet, all sheep
and oxen, and also the beasts of the field, the birds of the air,
and the fish of the sea; whatever passes along the paths of the
sea." In this parallel to the creation story we find, in the place
where Gen. 1.26 speaks of creation in the image of God, the
statement that God cares for Man and concerns Himself with
him. According to this the image of God obviously does not
mean that Man has some particular ability or shape which
distinguishes him from the rest of the natural world. This
passage has rather the simple sense, that the eternal God raises
this little creature to His own level, and makes Man His companion, His *alter ego*, His partner, His "Thou," with whom He
can hold converse, as a man converses with his equals. God
brings him into His personal society. Thus the prominent position of Man in relation to the whole creation rests by no means
on his higher birth, but solely on the unique relationship which
God has established with him. This is the supreme proof of the
sovereignty of God over all worldly differences of rank, that

He takes a living creature from his station in the ranks of the rest of creation, and by an act of election lifts him right up to His own level. This explains the fact that both in the eighth Psalm and in the book of Genesis Man's world dominion is deduced from the relationship which God has established with this creature. Because God has received Man into personal intercourse with Himself, He can give him the commission to rule over creation with divine authority. The ruling position of Man thus does not depend on the technical control over nature of which he is capable. God gives to Man, with whom He has established this personal intercourse, a share of His own dominion over the world. Because God has made Man His companion, it is a sin against God, a blood-guiltiness, a *crimen laesae majestatis*, if the life of a man is harmed. "Whoever sheds the blood of man, by man shall his blood be shed" (Gen. ix.6). As soon as Man loses his relationship with God, he sinks down again automatically to the level of the beast, and loses his royal right to rule. Indeed he can sink even lower than the beast.

If this is the sense of the verse in which the Bible describes the creation of Man, then this affirmation of faith in Man is in fact not affected nor even shaken by the scientific knowledge that Man's biological descent is from the widely-ramified family tree of the organic world, from which an earlier offshoot produced the man-like primates. For the same event, which from one point of view is the long and complicated history of evolution, out of which came the family tree of Man's ancestors with its many branches as we saw above, from the standpoint of eternity appears as a single act of God's creation, in which He created this people. And it is not only the total process of growth which, seen from the other side, is a work of God; for at the critical points in this history, by acts of selection and election, coming from the dimension of eternity, new distinctions are constantly decreed, which only become visible to us when we become aware of the divine order in our own personality. According to the Scriptures, the birth of Man on the sixth day of creation is such an act of election. Of course, the priestly narrator was thinking of ordinary days with morning and evening. But the wonderful thing in this story, which as we read it constantly makes us think that an invisible hand must have guided the pen of the writer, is the fact that in the

Biblical account of the work of the sixth day of creation the great stages of evolution are described in the same order in which, according to the discoveries of palaeontology, they occurred in the course of the immense period of 1500 million years.

It is, therefore, not unnatural, and in no way an attempt at apologetic harmonising, if one is here reminded of the ancient saying, which in the New Testament refers to the last days of the world in the future, but which we may equally well refer to the first beginnings of the world: "But do not ignore this one fact, beloved, that with the Lord one day is as a thousand years, and a thousand years as one day" (II Pet. III.8).

We must therefore conclude that the Biblical narrative of the six days of creation, written at a time when our modern knowledge of biology was not yet available, and when our astronomical measures of time were unknown, revealed with a retrospective prophecy, as in a grand vision of marvellous clarity, the plan of creation in all its architectonic grandeur from the foundation to the crowning consummation in the creation of Man. The palaeontological record of the present day can therefore only have as its function to explain in all its detail, with the help of the abundant material supplied by modern discoveries, the monumental building of which the plan is here brought before our eyes in its main outlines. Thus the birth of Man is an act of divine selection, by which God took this creature, who forms the crowning consummation of the many-branched tree of life, and at a particular stage of his evolution raised him out of his environment to His own level, in order to enter into personal dialogue with him which, when it has once begun, can never cease. This election of Man is expressed in the Jahwistic narrative when it says: "The Lord God took the man and put him in the garden of Eden to till it and keep it" (Gen. II.15). According to this God takes this creature out of the system of racial history, and directs him to a district which is geographically congenial, to a spot where He appoints him a special task, to prepare him for the high commission which is to be entrusted to him in the plan for the world. According to the Jahwistic narrative, this central event stands in the centre of world history. The creation of the plant world and the animal world has taken place with this in view, only for the sake of Man. God wills to make for this creature, for whom He has so high a mission, a habitat where fruits grow and living creatures breed, who will deliver him from his loneliness.

This act of elevation of a creature to human dignity is, according to the Bible story, the point of contact where the so-called history of salvation begins. This consists of nothing but decrees, which bring men face to face with decisions having eternal significance. All these decrees exist outside the material system of causality. For this reason the calling of God is not a causal determination, and so is not compulsion but a summons to decision. By reason of the fact that God brings Man into His presence, there are always only two ways open to Man. The one way is that of voluntary, unreserved surrender. When Man takes this way, God can lead him to the rank of royal ruler for which He has predestined him. When he refuses the call he does not simply sink back into the same state as other creatures, which God has not honoured with so high a vocation. For when God has so highly exalted a creature, this cannot simply be cancelled by his failure. There remains then only a second, sinister possibility: the creature whom God has honoured with His society can fall lower than any other creature. When he refuses God, Man must turn against God, and in demonic rebellion be driven to Satanic self-deification and self-adoration. According to the Scriptures, in the beginning Man succumbed to the Satanic temptation to follow this second way. But in spite of Man's failure, God has not abandoned him. And so, following the first act, in which God exalted Man to human dignity, there comes a second act, in which God calls to repentance Man who has neglected his calling. With this the great drama of redemption is begun, in which God, by the repeated sending of His messengers will attain His last goal, the homecoming of the Prodigal Son to his Father's house, which Christ has reopened.

From all that has been said it is clear that the Biblical explanation of the dignity of Man is fundamentally different from the way in which the extra-Biblical views of the world, above all the Greeks in the Platonic interpretation of Man, conceive of the superior status of Man. According to the Greek view, which has permeated modern thought in many forms since the age of rationalism, the dignity of Man rests on his constitution. In contrast to the animals, Man has an immortal soul, which has taken up residence only temporarily in his mortal body. Or, to put it in another way, the eternal element in Man is νοῦς (reason) or, as Raymond de Sabunde[8] expresses it, *cogitare* as distinct from mere *esse*, *vivere*, and *sentire*. As a result of this view Man is filled with an aristocratic darkness in relation to the animal world. The animals are despised as inferior beings. As the member of an ancient noble family is proud of his pure ancestry, which for centuries has never been blemished by any admixture with the blood of a bourgeois family, so it appears to Man as a disgrace and a humiliation to be in any sort of blood-relationship with the animals. For this Greek understanding of Man, which from paganism has permeated even Christian scholasticism, it is a grievous shock when palaeontology comes across bridge forms which bring to light the link between human beings and the animal world. On the other hand, the Biblical explanation of the dignity of Man is in no way threatened by the excavation of these transitional forms, but is only set in a clearer light. For according to the Scriptures the majesty of God is most plainly manifested in the fact that God can take a humble creature out of his relationship with the rest of the created world, and by a sovereign act of election exalt him to His own level. For the Biblical history of election it is therefore no refutation, but rather a confirmation, when it is proved that human capabilities (seen apart from this divine election) are developments of animal tendencies. Our eternal destiny depends, according to the Scriptures, not in any way on any physical or spiritual qualities which we carry in ourselves, but solely on a decision of God, who exalts us from our creaturely humility and gives us an eternal purpose. Luther, in a famous passage of his commentary on Genesis, accordingly bases the immortality of Man on this one foundation only when he says: "He who speaks with God or with whom God speaks – whether in wrath or in grace – he is truly immortal. The Person of the God who speaks and the Word indicate that we are creatures of such a kind, with whom God will speak till eternity, and in an immortal way."

[8] Raimundus de Sabunde, author of a fifteenth-century book entitled *Theologia naturalis sive liber creaturarum specialiter de homine et de natura eius inquantum homo*.

PART TWO

THE FUTURE OF THE WORLD

CHAPTER 1

THE FUTURE OF THE WORLD AS FORESEEN BY NATURAL SCIENCE

As we have said in all the previous sections, world history moves steadily forward in the form of time. The form of time consists in this, that everything that happens is first of all future, then becomes present, and then changes into the unalterable state of the past. As long as the event is still future, it is uncertain; only when it hardens into the past does it assume a fixed form. "The past stands still for ever." For our practical life, however, the future, which moves towards us relentlessly and to meet which we move forward, is alone important. In the section on the problem of causality we saw that the causal investigation of events has always only one aim, to illuminate the darkness of the future, since it is of crucial importance for all the decisions which we have to make at the present moment. The more light is shed on the darkness of the future, the better for our conduct in the present. Every light which at least in some degree illuminates the darkness of the future is valuable for us. Therefore the question which we put to natural science is this. Does it provide us with any certainty about the future and the end of the world? To this burning question science has only one answer, the prospect of so-called heat-death. What are we to understand by this? To understand the nature of heat-death, we must start from the law of the conservation of energy, as J. R. Mayer formulated it for the first time in 1842.[1]

Mayer applied the law first to the relation of heat and mechanical work. He determined the "mechanical heat equation" by calculating how much power of friction is necessary to raise the temperature of one gramme of water by one degree. Later the law was applied to chemical and electrical processes

---

[1] In an essay in *Liebigs Annalen der Chemie* entitled "Über die Kräfte der unbelebten Natur" ("On the forces of inanimate nature").

also. For example, a comparison was made of the energy
required to produce a quantity of water by combining hydrogen
and oxygen, with the energy which must be used to separate
the water into its constituent elements again by passing an
electric current through it. Meanwhile more recent observations
in all departments had confirmed Mayer's surmise that the law
of the conservation of energy determines, not merely the relation
between heat and mechanical work, but that it is a universal
law embracing all energetic processes. Modern physics too has
acknowledged that Mayer's law has survived all the profound
changes which have taken place in physics since his time.[2]

Every forecast about the future of the world must start from
this law. Wherein lies its significance for the future of the
world? To understand this, we must take the exact formulation
of the law as our basis. It runs as follows. In a closed system, the
quantity of energy contained therein remains constant. What
changes is only the form which this energy assumes (heat,
mechanical work, electric current, and so on). The quantity
of energy continually appears, but in new forms, like an actor
disappearing behind the curtains, changing his costume, and
then returning to the stage. A closed system is a system into
which no energy is introduced from outside, and from which no
energy can be lost. If we start from the exact formulation of the
law of energy, there would seem to follow from it quite a simple
consequence for the question of the future of the world: the
universe cannot perish; for is it not a closed system? The
masses of energy which are stored up in the universe can undergo the most manifold transformations, they can assume ever
new forms, they can even be dispersed, as heat is dispersed in
a cold room. But they cannot disappear from the endless space
which comprises the universe. None of this energy can ever be
lost.

When we concentrate on Mayer's law of the conservation
of energy by itself, we are indeed led to the view of the future
of the universe which W. Hauer[3] contrasts with the picture of

[2] The latest doubt, whether the principle of energy, in its familiar form, remains
valid for astrophysics, in the case of the Supernova of the year 1054, now the
Cancer nebula, is to be found in P. Jordan, *Schwerkraft und Weltall*, Brunswick
1952, p. 173.

[3] The Tübingen professor whose writings were the basis of the German Christian
Movement, formed in 1935.

the Christian hope. According to this German vision the universe is an eternal rhythm of life, which ebbs and flows in eternal deeps of creation. The teaching of Hinduism had already spoken of a twilight which constantly invades the whole universe. Life sinks into an abysmal depth of peace. Then once more the waves of life mount up out of the divine deeps, and once again new worlds and new beings appear in the light of a new day of creation. And so it goes on for ever. For life is eternal. In Germanic religion too there is the belief that there comes a time when *Midgard*, the human world, and *Asgard*, the world of the gods, fall in ruins together. But this does not mean annihilation. They fall into the eternal ground of creation, out of which they first came. And so a new world rises again from the ground. In the Nordic saga we read: "See arise again land from the floods, fresh and verdant. Waterfalls foam; the eagle soars, pasturing flocks of fish upon the crags." So we have a creative life, working without end, continually reducing everything back to itself, in order to give birth to it again from the fertile womb.

This belief in the inexhaustible abundance of life in the world was at one time represented by Ernst Häckel,[4] who disseminated it in the circles of the Social Democratic labour movement as a monistic doctrine. Under the Third Reich it was propagated in a new form as a "Germanic World Vision." There is something thrilling about the belief that the world can be constantly rejuvenated and recreated out of its own resources. But the question is, whether this is at all tenable from the standpoint of modern science. This is only certain to be the case if Mayer's law of the conservation of energy is the only foundation on which we may erect our conclusions about the future of the universe. But soon after Mayer had formulated the principle of energy, two other scientists, Clausius (1850) and Thomson (1851), laid down a second principle, which did not abolish Mayer's law of energy, as Häckel mistakenly thought, but amplified and supplemented it particularly in a certain direction. This is the so-called second principle of thermodynamics, or the law of entropy. Mayer's principle, which has since been described as the first law, is only the

[4] Ernst Häckel, *The Riddle of the Universe at the Close of the Nineteenth Century*, trans. Joseph McCabe, New York 1900.

purely quantitative law which controls all processes of transformation, irrespective of the direction in which they take
place. One can cause two chemical substances to form a compound and thereby use up chemical energy. But one can also
reverse the process and analyse the compound into its constituent elements, thereby producing chemical energy. We can produce heat by work. But on the other hand, heat can perform
mechanical work as, for example, in a steam engine. For the
first principle it is immaterial in which of these two directions
the conversion of energy occurs. But now the question arises,
in which of the two directions do the natural processes actually
take place? If we know this, a forecast about the future is
possible. The second principle, or the law of entropy, is the law
which determines the direction in which under normal conditions the conversion of energy actually occurs in the universe.

Chwolson speaks of the discovery of this law by Clausius
and Thomson with enthusiasm. He says: "I maintain that the
discovery of this law is the highest achievement of the human
mind in any department of knowledge and understanding
hitherto; that the idea which lies behind this law is unparalleled
in its philosophical depth, in its comprehensive significance
for the knowledge of existence, in its endless fruitfulness; and
that no science can point to any result, any idea, which is comparable in greatness to the law of entropy. Mankind can be
prouder of this law, which is impressed with the stamp of
absolute truth, than of all its other attainments and achievements. For almost everything else is either controversial or only
true to a limited extent. Among the eternal truths of reality
which mankind has succeeded in grasping, the law of entropy
stands pre-eminent." "The law of entropy is incomparably the
mightiest instrument which physics possesses for the investigation of the most secret, undreamt of laws controlling physical
phenomena."

What is the meaning of this idea, which has given the second
law its name, the idea of entropy? The word is a compound
from the Greek ἐν (= in) and τρέπειν (= to turn, veer, give
direction to). Entropy accordingly means "being directed
inwards." Entropy is thus the "degree of dispersion" of energy,
or the "inconvertibility value," the degree of "no-longer-
convertibleness," or the reduction of the availability and trans-

formability of energy. According to the law of entropy, in all natural processes this no-longer convertible value tends to reach a maximum. Nature has, as the physicists say, "a preference" for this direction. If, for example, two bodies at different temperatures influence each other, say two quantities of water which come together in the same vessel or two bodies which are exchanging radiation, then the warmer body will never become still warmer at the expense of the cooler, although according to the law of energy that would unquestionably be possible; but the warmer will always grow cooler for the benefit of the cooler body. The difference of temperature, as the capacity to perform work externally, will more and more be lost in the process. When the difference of temperature is completely equalised, and the energy is no longer capable of performing any work at all, then the maximum of entropy has been reached.

One might in the first place consider the law of entropy simply as one of the many laws which, like the law that "friction produces heat," for instance, or the law *omne vivum ex ovo*, do no more than summarise in a formula what has been observed within a limited circle of the world of experience, without making possible any more general conclusions about the universe. The law of entropy suddenly takes on a universal and cosmological meaning when this barrier is broken down and it is applied, not only to a definite circle of energetic processes, but to the universe as a whole. Then the law becomes the light which shines in the darkness of the future of the world; then the law of entropy is no longer merely an experimental law of thermodynamics, but gives its stamp to the whole course of the world for all time to come. It was Clausius who, in 1863, first ventured to take the eventful and perhaps fateful step, and exalted the law of entropy to a universal law. Since then there has lowered over mankind, like a dark thundercloud which will one day shed its load, the picture of "the death of the universe." Since then there is talk of "ice-death" or "heat-death," that is of the final state in which the whole sum of energy in the universe will have dissolved into masses with equal temperatures and equal radiation. According to Dubois-Reymond too, "scientific eschatology" consists in the expectation of the point in time, to which the world relentlessly draws near, in which all life of the mind and with it all knowledge will be extinguished, all ideas will be annihilated, along with all works of art and cultural achievements.

The view of modern physics will be made plain if we quote from the exposition of C. F. von Weizsäcker, set out in his lecture *Die Geschichte der Natur* ("The History of Nature").[5] For the sake of the importance of the subject, we shall reproduce the views of this influential physicist here in his own words.

Weizsäcker too, in discussing the problem of the future of the world, refers to the law of entropy, which he interprets as follows:

"The Second Law is concerned with the conversion of heat into other forms of energy. Let us limit our consideration to the conversion of heat into kinetic energy and *vice versa*. The steam engine shows that heat can turn into kinetic energy, and the heating of a body by friction shows that kinetic energy can turn into heat. But the relation between kinetic energy and heat is not altogether symmetrical. A body can turn its entire kinetic energy into heat, for instance, when it is brought to a complete stop by friction. But a body cannot turn its entire heat content into kinetic energy. The steam in the engine, at best, cools down to the temperature of its surroundings. The heat energy that is then left in the steam can no longer be turned into work, since the excess pressure in the cylinder was due only to the excess temperature of the steam. Only differences in temperature are capable of performing work; heat that is evenly distributed is a form of energy which may well be the result of work, but which cannot be converted back into work. Hence the production of heat is to some extent irreversible. We have defined a certain term, called entropy, as a measure of that heat content of a body which is no longer capable of performing work. With the help of this term, the Second Law may now be formulated as follows: the entropy of a closed system may increase or remain constant, but it cannot decrease. As long as no other forms of energy are converted into heat it remains constant. Otherwise it increases.

"Since in practice every event in nature produces heat – though often very small amounts – every event is in the strictest

[5] Stuttgart 1948. Eng. edn. *The History of Nature*, trans. F. D. Wieck. London 1951, pp. 52ff.

sense irreversible. Every pendulum comes to a standstill. Even the motion of the planets around the sun is constantly slowed down ever so little by interstellar gas. Hence, no event in nature is repeated exactly. Nature is a unique course of events. The final state would be one in which all motion has come to rest, and all differences of temperature have been equalised. This state has been called 'heat death.' Every closed system on earth, excepting only long-lived radio-active matter, reaches this state within observable time. That the course of events on earth continues at all is possibly only because there is a constant influx of energy in the rays of the sun – in other words, only because the earth is not a closed system. But given enough time, no structure in the universe should be able to escape heat death. It is conceivable, of course, that certain forms of energy, such as the energy of atomic nuclei or the kinetic energy of stellar bodies moving in empty space would never be converted into heat at all. But even then, there would be in the end no longer any conversion of energy.

"Against the application of the Second Law to the world as a whole, the objection has been raised that the world as a whole may not be a closed system – if, for instance, it is unlimited in extent. But this theoretical objection does not change our conclusions appreciably. The course of events in a finite part of the world would continue forever only if energy were forever flowing into it from the surroundings. As far as we know the world, there is no such influx of energy. On the contrary, all the stars are constantly losing energy by radiation into empty space. The concrete model of the universe of which I spoke above is surely moving towards heat death. When I said earlier that the uniqueness of the course of the world could be established with the help of one simple supplementary assumption, I meant the assumption that no unlimited supplies of heat are furnished to the world from outside.

"It might be said, however, that the Second Law is merely a special empirical law of terrestrial physics, and that nothing compels us to accord it equal validity for far-off spaces and times in the universe. I should answer, first, that we are already applying the Second Law in astrophysics, with good success. Of course, this fact alone does not prove that the Second Law remains valid even beyond the temporal limits of our knowledge in space and time. I might say further that the Second Law is not just any empirical law. In fact it can be derived from principles so basic that it would be difficult to conceive of circumstances so different that the law would be no longer valid. This derivation of the Second Law is supplied by what is called its statistical interpretation.

"Heat – or to be more exact, that physical state which produces the sensation of heat – is a disordered movement of the atoms. This fact is now well established experimentally. Hence, heat energy is really kinetic energy. When a moving body because of friction converts its kinetic energy into heat, the atoms in the body do not thereby stop moving. Before, they were all moving in the same direction, thus producing the visible movement of the whole body. Now, each atom is moving to and fro restlessly within a small space, while only the centre of gravity of the body is at rest. What appears to us a transition from motion to heat is actually a transition from ordered to disordered motion. Expressed in these terms, the Second Law states that ordered motion can be converted completely into disordered motion, but that disordered motion cannot be converted completely into ordered motion."

So far we shall follow Weizsäcker's account.[6] For readers who are interested in mathematics (others may skip the following pages) we add here how Weizsäcker gives an exact formulation to the law of entropy, and so makes it capable of proof:

"In order to make this statement exact and thereby capable of proof, we must find a mathematical definition for the concept of disorder. We must find a way to measure the degree of disorder. This is accomplished by the distinction between macro-states and micro-states. The macro-state of a body we call the state of the body such as it is defined by its directly measurable thermodynamic characteristics like pressure, temperature, density, etc. A body whose thermodynamic characteristics are known is a well-defined macro-state. But the micro-state of the same body could be defined only with the help of measurements of ultra-microscopic precision and completeness. We shall assume that the micro-state of the body is characterized

[6] A criticism of this argument from the law of entropy to the end of the world is to be found in C. Isenkrabe, *Energie, Entropie, Weltanfang, Weltende*, Trier 1910, and *Untersuchungen über das Endliche und das Unendliche*, Bonn 1920.

by the indication of both the position and the speed of every single atom. In practice, micro-states can never be known, they can only be delimited statistically. To this end they are correlated to certain micro-states. There is, of course, a certain macro-state corresponding to every micro-state, since the behaviour of all the atoms together determine the value of the gross characteristics that can be measured. But it is not true that there is one single micro-state corresponding to every macro-state. There are many more different micro-states than macro-states. For example, the temperature of a body indicates the average kinetic energy of the heat motion of its atoms – but in a total of 10^{23} atoms, there is a large number of different states of motion each of which has the same average kinetic energy per atom. The number of different micro-states corresponding to one certain macro-state can be used, now, as a characteristic in the definition of that macro-state. The micro-states cannot be distinguished from one another 'macroscopically,' but actually they are different. Their number is called the thermodynamic probability of the macro-state. This term expresses the thought that, the greater the number of micro-states in any given macro-state which we shall call A, the greater is the probability that any micro-state chosen at random will belong to this macro-state A. This thermodynamic probability now is the measuring rod of disorder for which we have been looking. Ordered motion is one whose macroscopic characteristics already indicate its micro-state with great accuracy. For example, if the only motion of the atoms in a body is represented by the motion of the body as a whole, then I know the direction and speed of all the atoms as soon as I know the direction and speed of the body as a whole. In this case, there is one single micro-state corresponding to the macro-state, and the motion is completely ordered motion. On the other hand, in a macro-state of a very high thermodynamic probability the knowledge of the characteristics of the macro-state tells us almost nothing about the motions of the atoms. In that case, the state of motion is greatly disordered.

"The Second Law, now, follows from consideration of probability. Let us assume we are dealing with a body which, at a certain moment, is in a macro-state A, of a relatively low thermodynamic probability. For brevity let us say that the body is in an improbable state. In what direction is this state likely to change? We can neither watch nor predict in detail the motions of the individual atoms. Thus, we can say only that the body is going to change into some other micro-state, of which we know beforehand merely that it will be one of the possible states close to state A – a state, that is, whose macroscopic characteristics are not too much different from those of A. Among these neighbouring states there must be those with a higher and those with a lower thermodynamic probability. The most probable thing is obviously that the body will change into one of those states whose probability is higher than that of A. Consequently, in the majority of cases the change will go in the direction of the higher probability, will keep on changing in that direction, on and on, until it reaches finally the state of highest probability. In this state it is then going to remain. Now the body has a maximum of disordered motion, that is of heat: it has achieved 'heat death.'

"These reflections show that the course of events claimed by the Second Law occurs not with certainty but merely with probability. But the number of atoms is so tremendously large that variations from the statistical mean occur practically never, except in microscopically small bodies. Speaking merely in terms of energy, it is possible that a stone on the ground might cool off and, with the help of the kinetic energy freed by the cooling, jump up into the air. But this has never happened, and never will. There has not been enough time since the beginning of the world for such an event even to become probable to any appreciable degree. It is still less probable that large portions of the world should reverse their direction of development. Entropy, it has turned out, is a measure of thermodynamic probability (namely, its logarithm). Consequently, the law that originally ran thus: It is probable that the thermodynamic probability of a body's state will increase – this law may now be formulated empirically: It is certain that the entropy of a body will increase. "Physicists have a habit of using commonplace or quaint examples to illustrate an abstract train of thought. Let us suppose a vast desert in which Arabs on their camels are riding hither and thither. In this desert there is a small hill. We define a micro-state for each Arab by indicating precisely the spot where he just happens to be. But we shall call 'macro-state' the indication whether an Arab is on the hill or not. The macro-state 'not on the hill' is far more probable than the macro-state 'on the hill,' since the size of the hill is very small compared with that of the entire desert. If the Arab is on the hill today, I can predict practically with certainty that he will not be on the hill tomorrow. [If he is not on the hill today, then it follows with almost the same certainty that he will still not be on the hill tomorrow.][7] Entropy acquires the highest possible value, if it does not have it already, and retains that value if it has it. That all the Arabs should be on the top of the hill by chance is virtually impossible. But if they should have met there once – for instance, by appointment – they will soon afterwards be scattered all over the desert. Such is the probability of increase in disorder. What is more, we must remember that the Arabs, as conscious beings, can decide to do something improbable, while the atoms cannot.

"It is difficult to conceive of circumstances that would invalidate the statistical proof of the Second Law. Fundamentally, there are fewer empirical elements in this law than in any other law of physics. However, I want to call attention to a premise of the Law that is often overlooked. That is the structure of time. . . .

"Let us study once more the improbable macro-state A. We assume this state to prevail at this moment. To the question, in what state will the body be in the immediate future, the answer must be: In a more probable macro-state. That is the Second Law. But if we ask, in what state has this body been in the immediate past, the answer, apparently with the same degree of probability is once more: In a more probable macro-state. For, if the Arab is on the hill today it is equally probable that he has not been there yesterday, and that he will not be there tomorrow. Yet it is obvious that our example fails when applied to the past. The answer we get for the past is empirically false. It contradicts the Second Law. According to the Second Law, the probability of a state is constantly increasing. Therefore, in the immediate past the body must have been in a less probable state than it is now. Why is it that the same method of drawing conclusions is true for the future, and false for the past?

[7] This sentence in the original German is omitted in F. D. Wieck's translation.

"The conclusion rests on the idea of probability. Probability is the quantitative expression of the idea of possibility. Future events are possible. That is why it makes sense to ask how probable they are. Past events are factual. We simply do not ask with what degree of probability this or that past event would lead up to the present, because the event has already occurred. There is no need to predict the event with a certain degree of probability, for it is known, or at least can be known, with certainty. At first the considerations show merely that we cannot draw conclusions of this sort with reference to the past, since of the past more is known than of the future. Probability, clearly, is an idea that is meaningful only where there is no certainty. But that the Second Law must necessarily have been just as valid in the past can be proved by the reflection that every moment in the past was at one time a moment in the present, and at that time conclusions about the future had to be based on probability. The historic character of time is usually assumed with a naïveté that causes us to overlook its importance in establishing the Second Law.

"These reflections all make it clear that the historic character of time is far from being merely a subjective quality of human experience. Or conversely, we might say these reflections show how impossible it is for us even to conceive of the objects of physics without referring them to a subject capable of knowing them. Atomic physics has made this fact familiar to us. In reality, however, our reflections show how unnatural is a system which on principle separates subject and object – as classical natural science did. As far as the Second Law is concerned, however, we may conclude that if we were to abandon it for the distant past, or for the distant future, we would by implication be assuming that in those distant ages the past did not consist of what has happened and is factual, and the future does not consist of what is to come and is possible.

"Can we at last arrive at a more concrete conclusion about the beginning of the world? Every finite part of the world has only a finite number of clearly distinguishable macro-states. Since every part passes through each of its states only once, it has only a finite reserve of possible distinguishable 'events.' In this formulation, the revolution of one star around another in a manner that does not change for millions of years is not considered as an event but as a stable macro-state. If events follow upon each other with finite speed, they must also run out in finite time. It follows, not only that there is an end in heat death awaiting the events, but also that events must have had a beginning in time. It is equally easy to conceive that events have begun all at once, or that they have grown slowly out of infinite eventless time, asymptotically, in the same manner in which heat death is generally reached. How meaningful it would still be to apply the concept of time to an eventless interval, that is a question which I shall leave open."

Let us look once more at this summary account of the attitude of modern scientists to the question of the decline of the universe, and let us briefly summarise the results which have emerged. That the universe is faced with a heat-death cannot indeed be proved with mathematical certainty, but so much is sure: it is altogether improbable that the cosmos will escape this fate. It is just as improbable, for example, as that red ink, poured into a glass of water, should remain apart from the water, and rise at one side of the wall of the vessel while at the other side the water should remain unmixed. Or, to take another analogy, that the universe should be saved from heat-death is just as improbable as that a quantity of water put on a fire should freeze to ice. All such improbable possibilities are indeed physically conceivable, but in real practical life, according to the views of any intelligent person, they are absolutely out of the question. It is just as much out of the question that the universe should escape heat-death. Objections which have been raised by famous scientists such as Max Planck, Lord Kelvin, Bavink, and others against this, when carefully examined, all come to this, that some inexhaustible source of energy is assumed, from which new energy is constantly poured into the cosmos, either from without or from within, perhaps from the atoms. Thus every time it is the factor of infinitude that is being operated with. But in so doing we are always overstepping the limits of polar space, whose essence consists in the very fact that every value which appears in it bears the character of the finite. Yet we cannot assume an infinite source of power unless we reckon with Almighty God. And we may not have recourse to this so long as we are thinking in a purely scientific way.

All possible ways have already been tried, in order to imagine a world without God, which maintains itself in motion. It has been thought, for example, that the world might be constructed as a *perpetuum mobile*, that is like a clock which is constantly winding itself up again while working, and so goes on for ever. Against this it has been rightly objected that during every transition from the running down of the clock weights to a new motion some energy at least would be lost through friction. Even this interchange between running down and winding up would in the end, because of the exhaustion of power, become slower and slower and at last come to a standstill.

Thus all such attempts to escape heat-death remain futile. The only thing which can delude us into forgetting this dreary prospect is the thought that, if it is a matter of fifty million years away, then the world has still some time to develop and we need not be too much afraid of this prospect. All in all this is but a poor consolation; for we have known since Einstein that even the measure of time is only relative; the time-measurement of fifty million years is only that of a certain system of reference. This sytem of reference is not something objective and valid in itself. If, for example, we were to imagine motion at a rate near to the speed of light, that is 186,000 miles per second, the fifty million years which separate us from heat-death would shrink to a few hours. Even the length of time of the reprieve which has been given to the cosmos does not deceive us about the real situation of the universe. It is like the situation of a man condemned to death, who still has a fair interval of time between the verdict and the execution. This by no means alters the real situation, if the forecast made by leading scientists about the future of the world is correct.

Before we leave this point we must mention another astronomical forecast, which while it does not remove the ultimate prospect of heat-death, does modify to some extent the course which the earth, and hence mankind, must travel to that end.

It has become clear that the earth might become uninhabitable much earlier, through the occasional contrary process of an increase of the sun's radiation. The so-called *novae* (new fixed stars) are for the most part not new, but variable stars, the radiation of which occasionally increases five thousandfold to a hundred thousandfold; and in the process they blow off one ten-thousandth to one-thousandth of their mass as incandescent gas. This process has been observed more than once in the case of some of them, so that today the regular repetition of it can be reckoned with. It is true that Himpel's assumption that the sun is such a star and that its nova-eruptions have framed the limits between its geological ages,[8] has not been accepted; but the possibility of a further nova-eruption cannot be ruled out altogether. If this does not occur, the prospect for the sun and for the majority of the stars, according to Gamow (1948), is a gradual rise in their temperature. The basis for this view is that the helium derived from their hydrogen is less transparent and retains the heat until the temperature forces a sufficient outlet. As a result of this the surface radiation would rise in about ten million years to one hundred times its present rate. In the process all the water on the earth will be vaporised, and its atmosphere will become like that of Venus. Whether any living creatures could adapt themselves to these conditions cannot be said – human beings will probably not succeed in doing so, but in a long-drawn-out struggle in caverns underground they may try to maintain their life by means of refrigeration so long as their resources allow.

Thus we are faced with a forecast of the future of mankind which is far more dreadful than the ice-death which was prophesied earlier. For the tragedy that will be played when our last descendants must flee into caverns, and when all human beings throng together in order painfully to prolong their life a little while by means of refrigeration, is something which, if our imagination can paint the details even to some extent, must appear so dreadful and infernal that Dante's *Inferno* with its descriptions of the tortures of hell would seem a trifle compared with it. It goes without saying that this age would later be followed after all by the cooling off determined by the law of entropy.[9]

It is therefore only of speculative importance for mankind, if perhaps it can be assumed that this whole process might not be realised to the bitter end, because there are mathematical solutions for the variability of the dimensions of the cosmos,

[8] K. Himpel, *Erdgeschichte und Kosmogonie*, Leipzig 1940, rejected by F. Noelke in *Die Sterne*, xx (1940), p. 117.
[9] A. March, *Der Weg des Universums*, Bern 1948, p. 149.

according to which the expansion (the dispersal of the galaxies) would become slower, then reverse, and on contraction again lead to its original concentration, which is thus followed by a primordial explosion. Weizsäcker has shown that even this conception does not escape the law of entropy, although Tolman has ascertained that in the curved metric of Einstein there are more processes without increase of entropy than in the classical metric. The supply of forms of existence is finite.[10]

The fact remains that not only we human beings and all animals, but also the whole inorganic world, is faced with the fate of total annihilation. The whole creation is like a wood, through which the forester has gone with axe in hand, marking with a stroke every tree which is to be felled in the approaching deforestation. So every man, however young and healthy he may be, is already marked for death, and has a precisely predetermined time still to live, before it is his turn in the universal death which pervades the whole creation.

Regarded from the standpoint of modern physics, and in view of Heisenberg's new theory of light, the following has still to be said about heat-death. If we could be sure of the complete stability of the non-radioactive nuclei on the one hand, and the spatial closure of the universe on the other hand, then, as a fluctuating phenomenon, the return of ordered conditions in the universe might be conceivable at an unforeseeably remote period. But Heisenberg's theory of light[11] ascribes what is certainly a very low probability indeed to the development of nuclei from radiation; accordingly the converse might also be possible. Heat-death therefore appears to be somewhat less uniform today than formerly, though without giving any more satisfaction to our need to grasp the meaning of the universe. For in all these phenomena the entropy of the universe increases relentlessly all the time.

[10] C. von Weizsäcker, *The History of Nature*, p. 50.
[11] Spinor theory of light: see *Lexikon du Physik*, 1952.

CHAPTER 2

THE FUTURE OF THE WORLD IN THE LIGHT OF THE GOSPEL OF THE RESURRECTION

1. *The World as God's fallen Creation*

ACCORDING to the Bible, the world in which we live is a fallen creation, and its existence bears the sign of Paradise Lost. It is true that this view is rejected by a large part of the educated world as a myth, which must be surrendered to the prevailing process of demythologising. Yet no one who is involved in modern life can escape the impression that a profound truth underlies this myth. Nature and the world of mankind are affected through and through by a discordance, a painful wound, from which we all suffer in one way or another. We must first of all take notice of discordance as a simple fact, apart from any mythological explanations, before drawing any conclusions from it. In doing so we must to some extent proceed from the external to the internal and, before we examine the content of the modern world, we must first take a look at the form in which, according to our reflexions hitherto, it is irrevocably contained. This is the polar form of time and space, which we have constantly been coming across from the beginning. In order to link up what I have written in detail in the earlier volumes of this work with the basic ideas of modern physics, we must start with the identification of the two polar relations of subject-object and present-past. This means, to express it quite simply, that what appears to us as an objective thing is strictly speaking no longer present, but already belongs to the past. Thus we see the world, not as it is now at this moment, but only as it has been recently. The objective is no longer in the molten, fluid state of the present, but has already hardened into the unalterable past. Our starting-point is the universal law of polarity, to which all distinctions are subject.

The realm of polarity is divided into the realm of objectivity and the non-objective realm of the "we." If, to make it quite plain, we express it in mathematical terms, we obtain these two equations:

1. Realm of objectivity = Realm of the past;
2. Realm of the "we" = Realm of the present.

At the same time the realms which are here placed one above the other are in a polar relationship.

The relation "Realm of objectivity = Realm of the past" finds its most pregnant expression in physics in the special theory of relativity, Albert Einstein's contribution, which is based on this very fact that between the time of the event and the time of the observation of the event there lies a period of time which depends upon the state of motion. There is therefore no sense in speaking of events in different places as simultaneous. "Undoubtedly the belief in objective simultaneity is originally based on the fact that everyone takes for granted that the things he sees are set in the time of observation."[1]

The relation "Realm of objectivity polar with Realm of the 'we' " means not only that the world of objectivity and the sphere of the non-objective mutually affect one another, but that this polar relation is a dimensional one. Both these facts have been noticed by some physicists, in view of the epistemological difficulties in the precise definition of the concept of "observation." "In the same way it is now profitable to review the fundamental discussions, so important for epistemology, of the difficulty of separating the subjective and objective aspects of the world. Many of the abstractions that are characteristic of modern theoretical physics are to be found discussed in the philosophy of past centuries. At that time these abstractions could be disregarded as mere mental exercises by those scientists whose only concern was with reality, but today we are compelled by the refinements of experimental art to consider them seriously."[2]

It seems at first as if these were all merely mathematical,

[1] H. Weyl, *Raum, Zeit, Materie,* 5th edn. Berlin 1923, p. 144; Eng. edn. *Space—Time—Matter,* trans. H. L. Brose, London 1922.

[2] W. Heisenberg, *Die physikalische Prinzipien der Quantumtheorie,* 2nd edn. 1931, p. 49; Eng. edn. *The Physical Principles of the Quantum Theory,* trans. C. Eckart and F. C. Hoyt, Chicago 1930, p. 65.

abstract formulae about space-time dimensions. But on closer examination it soon becomes clear to us that even in these mathematical relations a profound dissonance is concealed, under which we suffer continually. It is only the mathematical expression of what Goethe summarises in these words: "Could I but say to this moment: Linger, for thou art so fair, fain would I let thee enchain me, a willing victim in thy snare." The world which we perceive does not truly belong to us at all, but is a reality which we are always groping after and never possess. Life in this world is thus a continual, tantalising torment. The only thing we can call our own, the present, escapes us at the very moment when we are about to clutch and possess it. And we are constantly overwhelmed with the mood which Hölderlin has expressed so incomparably in his *Song of Destiny*: "To us has been given no resting-place. Mortal men plunge and fall, like water tossed from rock to rock, down into the unknown for ever."

With these glimpses we have only touched in a preliminary way on the discordance contained in the primeval form of time, when we identify the relation of present and past with the relation of subject and object. This discordance becomes still deeper when we take notice of the other primeval relation between I and Thou. The painful disharmony involved in the I–Thou relationship is at once noticeable to us whenever we study this relationship in the sphere of human affairs. But as we have seen, this relationship has a polar structure. The original force of the I–Thou relationship produces this result, that nothing but my own ego is immediately given to me, that nothing but the joys and sorrows of this single ego are directly sensed by me. The joys and sorrows of all other people are beyond me. Even my nearest and dearest friend, even a sick relation who tosses in pain beside me while I sit by his bed; no matter how sympathetic my heart is, I can only faintly imagine what he suffers, with the help of my powers of insight and compassion. Here the hard law applies: "Everyone is his own neighbour," Max Stirner, a contemporary of Ludwig Feuerbach, in his book *Das Einzige und sein Eigentum*, derived a purely egotistical ethic from this undeniable elementary fact. In his opinion all altruistic commandments, all state constitutions and economic systems, are nothing but subtle attempts to rob me of this unique possession, and to make me in some way a servant of the so-called "public" or "society," which in reality is only a remote abstraction. Because my own ego with its joys and sorrows is the only thing I possess directly, it is in fact a tremendous temptation to me to do all I can to set this unique ego, which is so central for me, upon the throne; and to treat all others, who after all come in contact with me only as objects, and whose situation I can only with difficulty enter into, as means to be used for my own ends. The capacity which men like Himmler have in such high degree, of treading on corpses and looking on without remorse while others are tortured to death, is only the last and most terrible exaggeration of something which lies in each one of us, and which is the simple result of the fact that, in consequence of the polar structure of the I–Thou relationship, everyone else's world of experience is hermetically sealed to me, and that because of this, as Eberhard Grisebach says, the other person remains for me "an eternally strange Thou." Thus the temptation to all the deeds of cruelty which have filled us with horror, the explosive material for all family tragedies and all world wars, is already contained in the root-form of our existence, with which we are born into the world. This is seen with extraordinary plainness in certain facts which have constantly been observed in war-time. Whenever human beings are cooped up for any length of time in a confined space together, for example in a cattle-truck in which prisoners are transported, or in the same block in a concentration camp, even well-brought-up people in the end find it impossible to control themselves and to restrain the irritability which rises up involuntarily against every fellow-man who stands in their way and restricts their living-space. The confined space becomes hell. "Everyone becomes his neighbour's devil."

In hunger camps people had a similar experience. As long as hunger is kept within moderate bounds, the rules of respectable society can be maintained. They act as a counterpoise to crass egoism. But whenever hunger reaches a certain point, all moral and legal usages suddenly collapse like houses of cards. Respect for the property of one's neighbour, and the inbred prohibition of stealing, are swept away like an annoying hindrance, and the primitive disposition, which was in us before all our polite training, and which has its roots in the whole form of existence, erupts with volcanic force out of the depths. The savage in man breaks loose, and brutal egoism demands its rights.

The fact that we are here dealing with the primitive forms of our whole existence is made still more plain if we look beyond the sphere of our human life, and, in accordance with the purpose of this book, take into consideration the whole of creation, within which our human life is but a tiny section. Let us glance first at the animal world.[3] Among the animals there are no criminal types, no asocial elements to be blamed for the frightfulness which prevails everywhere in the animal world. There are no gangsters who bring whole nations under their power, terrorising them and devising the most refined methods of torturing other creatures to death. The animals are not individuals at all in the sense that we human beings are. Each single animal is merged in its class. Its life follows rules which have been fixed for hundreds of thousands of years. Its conduct is controlled by the rhythm of life prescribed by its species. For this very reason we see in animal life even more plainly than in human life the structural law of the original relationships in which all creatures stand to each other. It is true that real international wars with methodically equipped armies exist in the animal world only between the ant states and termite hills, with their soldiers marching to fight against each other. But wherever there live together different kinds of animals which are dependent on one another for their food, for example in a wood or in a marshy pool of water swarming with living creatures, or in the sea, a constant state of war prevails. No creature's life is safe even for a moment. It is in constant danger, and murder may lurk everywhere. Clandestine assaults are the order of the day. The spider has its cunning net laid out to catch its prey; as soon as a fly enters the net, the spider flings itself upon its victim and devours it, while it resists in agonised desperation. The hawk comes out of the wood and circles over the poultry-yard, where the hens in nameless fear of death are clustered together perhaps under a little stone bridge which leads over the brook, just as human beings swarm into the air-raid shelter during a bomber attack; then the bird of prey

[3] See the two books by F. W. Weber, *Gott in der Natur*, Berlin 1936, and *Der alt böse Feind*, Berlin 1937.

swoops down in slanting flight with its rolling yellow eyes upon a sturdy cock, strikes its claws deep into its flesh in spite of a stout resistance and crushes its skull. During the murder, which may be repeated at any moment, the other hens sit by rigid and paralysed with fright, and it is many hours before they recover from the shock of this experience. The lämmergeier falls upon the chamois from behind as it grazes peacefully beside a precipice, terrifies it with the beating of its wings and drives it to the edge, until it plunges into the depths and falls a helpless victim to its persecutor.

How shocking it is, that wherever a number of different animals live together, for example in a marshy lake or in the open sea, each kind of animal is the terror of the others! While themselves torturing and murdering, they are each constantly in danger of being attacked by bigger animals and suffering a painful death. While the seal is chasing the cod, mackerel, herring, and crabs, of which it requires fifteen to twenty pounds a day for its nourishment, it is every moment in danger of finding its deadliest foes emerging from the bottom of the seas, the cachalot and killer whales, for which the seal is a delicacy. The startled seal leaps many feet high above the surface of the sea when the murderer approaches, to escape from the terrible death that now threatens it. But those desperate leaps in the air are of no avail, when in spite of stout resistance it is sucked down by a whirlpool into the unfathomed deadly gorge of the devouring monster, where the stomach will narrow round it more and more, until at last it must be choked by the stupefying air pressure and meet a painful end.

In the last volume[4] an incident was described in which two animals in a tributary of the Amazon, one of which had been pounced on by the other, were suddenly attacked, while they were locked in a death struggle, by a shoal of carib-fish, with teeth sharp as razors, and became their helpless prey.

The tortures by which in all these cases animals put each other to death have nothing to do with the diabolic sadism with which a human criminal with a perverted imagination devises forms of vengeance, by which a hated enemy who has fallen into his hands can be made to suffer agony which can be repeated until he is "done in" and loses consciousness. Only a

[4] *The Transformation of the Scientific World View*, p. 254.

man could have written the terrible sentence of Nietzsche: "To watch suffering is sweet, to cause suffering is sweeter." The beast is quite harmless compared with man. Schopenhauer says: "Men are the devils of the earth." Nevertheless the cruelties which are the order of the day even in the animal world constantly remind us of what took place in the concentration camps, where men were fastened to the block and hanged on a tree. This is only possible because in the animal world too, although individual animals have no responsibility for the situation, the relation of every creature to the others is subject to the same fundamental rule that applies in human life. One living creature must continually squeeze out or devour other forms of life in order to preserve its own existence. The beasts, and especially the beasts of prey, are therefore equipped by nature with deadly weapons and instruments of torture, which they use in the fulfilment of their destiny. Consider the teeth of the carib-fish or the jaws of the lion and the tiger, or the talons of the hawk and the vulture. The animal which needs other creatures for its nourishment is so adapted that it has no restraint when it destroys these other creatures. The sufferings of its victims lie beyond the threshold of its consciousness and in no way affects its inner being.

This continuous state of war, this constant threat of impending danger, is not confined to the animal world, although it is only the sufferings of the animal world with which we human beings can to some extent sympathise, because the animals are "our unknown brothers."[5] The frontier between the animal world and the vegetable world which sustains it is, as we saw in *Christian Faith and Natural Science*, a fluid one according to modern research. There is only a difference of degree between the two. Fechner was therefore rightly of the opinion that it would be senseless to assume that animals live in the daylight of consciousness, while plants, which in other respects grow, beget, and reproduce according to the same biological laws, are surrounded by the night of complete unconsciousness. And it is a naïve piece of human arrogance, as we saw earlier, to suppose that the plants may have something like sensation, but that their mental life is at best a dreamy twilight state, and only our human consciousness is a state of clear awareness.

[5] Julie Schlosser, *Die unbekannten Brüder*, Berlin 1932.

In making such assertions we go beyond our competence. All that we can say is that the sensory life of plants is different from ours. We cannot think ourselves into this strange world. If even plants have sensation, then the fierce battles in which they must struggle for their lives when set upon by their deadly foes, must also be accompanied by pains which are probably no less than the sufferings which we experience when our life is at stake. In the tropical primeval forest, where everything grows wild with no forestry service to regulate the growth, the scene resembles a battlefield. Everywhere one sees mighty trees, overgrown and stifled with very strong and luxuriant parasitic plants which have sunk their roots into them. Some trees already lie like fallen giants on the ground, their rotting trunks serving as luxuriant root-soil for noxious growths. The rest still stand upright. But they too must in the course of time succumb to the deadly embrace, and, in the end, when their power of resistance has been broken, fall crashing to the ground. If we watch this death struggle in the plant world, perhaps in slow motion in a nature film – what in our life is but time to draw a breath, is a whole day in the life of a plant – we see the convulsive movements and death agonies which precede the withering of plants. We at least guess from afar something of the suffering which may accompany this strangulation, although as human beings we can have no conception of what takes place inside the organism of a plant when, for example, it is frosted on a cold night, or when it is defencelessly devoured alive by a horde of millions of phylloxera (of which one can in a single summer become the ancestress of thirty million descendants).

Modern research shows us that not only have the boundaries between the animal world and the plant world become fluid, but that even the walls dividing the whole organic world from inorganic nature, and so separating biology from physics, have at least in principle been broken down. For we know that an atom or a molecule is not a dead, homogeneous material particle, but a microcosm, pulsating with mysterious life, whose tiniest particles circle round each other with unimaginable velocity. We also know now, for example, that the individual viruses are living molecules, which feed on tobacco leaves, so that even a molecule can devour other creatures and can grow and multiply through their destruction. We must therefore ask: Should this rich and lively inner world of atoms and molecules, seemingly separated by no more than a difference of degree from the realm of primitive organic life, be utterly excluded from the light of consciousness in which the organic world exists? Does it have to be steeped in the light of unconsciousness? P. Jordan says: "We know nothing as to whether perhaps the molecules that are capable of multiplying possess some trace of sensation; for example, a slight presentiment of the pleasure which reproduction gives to us higher animals."[6] Even this leading physicist, who has not spoken his last word on this subject, cannot evade the question whether perhaps there may be struggle and strife even in the molecular world. Marie Curie, after long and thorough study of the process of radioactivity, could not avoid the impression that even in this realm of the smallest of all things it was no soulless mechanism that was revealed, but that there too there was a continual drama of battles, tragedies, murders, and suicides, accompanied by the most violent inner shocks. Naturally what goes on within the atoms and molecules is far more remote from our human experience than the mental life of animals and plants; it is quite hopeless for us to try to imagine this completely alien form of consciousness. But so much at any rate we must say, that the whole creation, not only the world of mankind, but also the world of animals and plants and inorganic nature, is subject to one common, fundamental law. Everywhere the principle of polarity prevails, although in the most diverse variations. Everywhere there reigns an unremitting warfare. Creatures, which need each other for their life, obstruct and destroy each other. The whole of nature is pervaded by an unsatisfied need. Paul can therefore speak in ch. VIII of his Epistle to the Romans of a groaning of the whole creation crying out for deliverance from the bondage of corruption.

All this brings us to the last and most decisive question. Is there a solution for this problem, or is it inevitable? Will the relentless law of the universe, to which all things are now subject, hold for ever, or does the "scheme of this world" come to an end at some time? This is the question of the destiny of the

6 P. Jordan, *Die Physik und das Geheimnis des organischen Lebens*, 6th edn. Brunswick 1948.

whole cosmos, and the personal fate of each one of us is involved in it.

Nietzsche could wax enthusiastic over the idea that we shall be whirled around in circles by this polar world system in a mad career for all eternity, as on a roundabout that we can never leap off. According to his view, upon every round of this wild ride we should show our delighted enthusiasm with renewed cries of Encore! We men of the second world war, who have passed through the hell of nights of bombing, and have experienced the pogroms or have seen the dust-carts in the concentration camps, on which the naked skeletons of our wasted brothers, packed together like sardines, were carried off to the furnaces – for us it is harder than it was for Nietzsche, who received his great inspiration, not among the ruins, but in the Engadine and in the sunny south, to clap our hands and cry Encore! We can no longer be enthusiastic about the eternal continuation of this polar world form, in whose dark bosom are contained all the fearful possibilities that have been realised in recent decades. For us there are only two possibilities. The first is that the world will in fact go on as at present. Then life is not worth living. The other possibility is the *hope* that history is not an eternal cycle, but a course which had a beginning and moves towards a goal, and that all the stations of the Cross through which we have passed are only a transitional stage on the way to this destination. But this destination must not be annihilation if everything is not to be utterly meaningless, but must be what the New Testament calls a *telos* (goal, end), in which not merely will some things in this world be improved and the gravest abuses find an end, but in which the whole basic form of this world will be abolished to make way for a new form.

2. *The Prehistory of the New Testament Easter Faith*

As long as men have not yet penetrated the deepest secrets of life, they still believe that the world may be led to the attainment of a goal within its present polar form, and that this goal gives a noble meaning to the world and a worthwhile purpose to our work. This can best be illustrated from the first stage in the development of the future hope of the people of Israel, which in this respect is also a historical example of man's wrestling with the ultimate problem of his life.

After the first severe political shocks had affected the people of Israel, a vision of the future appeared before the eyes of their prophets to which the people could cling in their distress, the "repair of the fallen house of David," that is to say a glorious restoration of the power which had once belonged to the nation in its heyday under its greatest king. When the burden became more grievous and the ground of their earthly existence began to shake under their feet, because the little nation was ground between the world powers as a grain of corn between millstones, and was forced to leave its destroyed capital city in a long procession of refugees into an alien land, the hope of the return of the former glory of the Davidic Kingdom faded from the hearts of the people. In place of the Davidic Kingdom there appeared all at once something altogether new, in which the radical transformation of all the conditions of this world was foreshadowed. In place of a new "Kingdom" there appeared a "new aeon" (*Olam haba*), a new age of the world. With this expectation the apocalyptic movement began. This new aeon, which took the place of the re-establishment of the Davidic state, was at first simply an idealisation of the prosperity and joy and beauty which the present aeon had brought. Men dreamed of an age in which the fields would bear crops twelve times, and men would grow to the stature of giants in the midst of a natural paradise, and in constant health and strength would reach a ripe old age. This second stage of eschatology, the hope of a new age of the world which would be an expanded and improved edition of the present age, has since been repeated again and again in new forms.

The most influential form of this secular end-hope was the Utopian expectation of Marxism, the dream picture of the state of the future, as Bebel attractively described it in his book *Die Frau*. When the class struggle has finally disappeared, the essential work in factories and on the land will be done without effort in a few hours per day with the aid of the latest achievements of mechanical technology. Everyone sets to work together, and the rest of the day will be free for the enjoyment of art and the noble pleasures of life. Another form of this secular vision of the future is the kingdom of world peace which the pacifists look forward to, and which Kant anticipated in his book *Zum ewigen Frieden* ("Perpetual peace"). A third form, which was only a short-lived dream, however, was the Nazi idea of a reform of national life under the leadership of a so-called master race.

All these visions of the future are only variations of the second stage of development, which was reached by Jewish eschatology as early as the period of II Esdras and the Apocalypse of Baruch. But this was not the end of the development. Now at last, when all political illusions had been utterly shattered, in the ordeal of deepest misery, the late fruit of apocalyptic ripened, the idea which can only be grasped by those who have plumbed the very depths of existence. This third stage in the development of human life appears as early as II Esdras, where it is written: "This age is full of sadness and infirmities. For the evil about which you ask me has been sown. . . . If therefore that which has been sown is not reaped, and if the place where the evil has been sown does not pass away, the field where the good has been sown will not come" (II Esdras IV.27ff.). In other words, it is not enough to pluck out the weeds which keep springing up in the soil of the present world. The transformation must be more radical and far-reaching. The whole soil which inevitably goes on producing these weeds must be done away with. The whole field, in which the germs of the weed seeds lie dormant, must disappear, and a completely new field must take its place. It is not enough to keep on cutting off the heads of the hydra, if new heads can grow again in their place. The whole monster must be mortally wounded. To drop the metaphors, it is not enough to fill this ground-form of world history, time, with a new content, so that the time of disaster and struggle is succeeded by a time of happiness and world peace. No, the whole form of temporality must be abolished. In the new aeon, as understood in this context, there will be no more hours, days, months, years. The flow of days and hours, this waterfall in which wave after wave plunges into the bottomless abyss, this eternal fleeting, falling, and melting, must vanish. *Corruptela peribit* (the corruptible itself will perish). The passing itself will be past. The whole principle of polarity will be abolished. This will make room for a new world form, for a new heaven and a new earth. This new world form — this is the decisive conviction of the late apocalyptists — exists altogether beyond the whole of our present imagination, comprehension, and understanding. For all our ideas are limited within the range of the polar world form. "But how canst thou, a mortal man, who livest in the corruptible world, grasp the eternal?" *Non potest corruptibilis in saeculo corruptibili cognoscere viam incorruptibilis.* Thus as children of this age of corruptibility our eyes are holden. We cannot behold the pure glory of the incorruptible world, any more than we can look at the sun with our earthly eyes without being blinded.

This third stage of development of the apocalyptic expectation was attained out of the very depths of the misery of the world. This most mature form of the idea of the expected end of the world was adapted in the New Testament and carried further, especially by Paul. For this is what strikes us when we read the New Testament, coming to it from Jewish apocalyptic or any of the modern variations: the whole fantastic idea of a golden age of the world, which had blossomed luxuriantly even in the penultimate stage of apocalyptic, the picture of an idealised, gigantically magnificent humanity in the midst of a natural paradise has suddenly and utterly vanished in the New Testament. Instead of all these fantastic descriptions of an eschatological hope within the world there appears something altogether different, something which in our present human language cannot be expressed positively, but only negatively, although it is the most positive reality that there is: "an inheritance which is imperishable, undefiled, and unfading" (1 Pet. 1.4), or expressed in substantives which indicate a totally new world situation, "imperishability," "glory," "power" (1 Cor. xv.42f.). The appearance of this totally new order of the universe is described by a unique expression, which we can only understand when we realise that it is not enough to fill time with a new and finer content, but that the whole form of time itself must be overcome and the content of the world, like molten metal, must be poured into a new mould. Paul says: "For this perishable nature must put on the imperishable, and this mortal nature must put on immortality. When the perishable puts on the imperishable, and the mortal puts on immortality, then shall come to pass the saying that is written: 'Death is swallowed up in victory' " (κατεπόθη ὁ θάνατος εἰς νῖκος, 1 Cor. xv.53ff.). Paul then compares the world form of the imperishable with a new dress, which the world, now wearing the perishable garment, will put on, and so to speak be clothed with it. Only when the world has received this fundamentally new form, of which we have at present no conception, will everything be fulfilled and solved which at present remains unfulfilled and unsolved.

It is only a hope that is here expressed in the first place. What about its fulfilment? Our personal wishes and the apocalyptic dreams of highly excited masses have not the slightest influence on this; for all too often it is true that world events take their course without respect to the passionate wishes of individual human beings and individual nations. Not all the demands which we, the little inhabitants of the earth, may make in the name of reason and of humanity can alter the course of events. All these demands are only variations on the well-known postulate of practical reason, which Kant formulated in the proof of immortality in his *Critique of Practical Reason*: "If the law of morality is to be valid, this life on earth must have a continuation in which worthiness to be happy and the enjoyment of happiness will not be separated, as in the present state of the world, but will really be in harmony with each other."[1] Similarly we can say: If life is to be worth living, there must come into being a state of the world in which everything will reach perfection which has only been a torso here, which has stopped short at its beginnings or has been broken off in the middle of its development. We can, of course, utter such "postulates" in a tone of emphatic conviction. But the greater question is just this, whether reality is governed according to our demands, whether the world has any meaning at all, or whether in the end everything perishes in the night of utter meaninglessness.

Our wishful thinking, our rational postulates, and our demands for meaning therefore carry us not a step further forward in this question. There is only one fixed point, an Archimedean point outside the whole of reality, from which the world we are a part of, this total reality involved in polarity, can be thrown off its hinges. That is the reality of God. We cannot attain to this, as we saw before, by our own efforts. God Himself must give us access to it. Only if God by His own initiative reveals Himself to us do we see "in His light" that the whole "scheme

---

[1] See Kant, *Critique of Practical Reason*, trans. T. K. Abbott, London 1927, pp. 218ff.

of this world," the whole polar world form, while not itself a guilt, as the Hindu religion of redemption assumes, is indeed the expression of an original Fall from God and a temptatio to estrangement from and forgetfulness of God. Only in the light of God do we realise that behind this temptation there is a power which seeks to separate us from God.

An inevitable consequence follows from this. If God exists, then everything which exists apart from Him must exist for His sake. Even the antagonistic power, which is the source of the temptation to estrangement from God, must utterly vanish. Even in the Old Testament Law all worship of other gods, apart from the God who is the only Lord, is suppressed in the majestic words: "For the Lord your God is a devouring fire, a jealous God" (Deut. IV.24, IX.3). The same word is addressed in the New Testament against disobedience to God's commandment (Heb. XII.29). God's omnipotence is here compared to a fire, perhaps to a spark thrown into a parched wood. The flame thus produced must spread with elemental force, and cannot rest until everything has gone up in flames. To drop the metaphor: if God exists, than a world form which represents a temptation to forgetfulness of God must finally be abolished.

In view of all that has been said, there is no possibility of this unless the event takes place which the apocalyptists refer to when they say that corruptibility itself must perish. Temporality must be restored to eternity. It is in the nature of time, as Heidegger says, that something is always "outstanding." Everything present is on the way to the future. It is always in process of becoming. This inconclusive, imperfect state must accordingly be replaced by the state of perfection. This is what the New Testament describes with the word "*telos*." This does not mean an end-point like the period at the end of a sentence or the final cadence of a musical composition, after which the music stops. Neither is it the return to undifferentiated unity, to the indifference beyond all contradictions, which is the expectation of Hindu religion. It is rather the entrance into a completely new world form, in which the past is, in Hegel's sense, "transcended," a new creation, a new heaven and a new earth. The world content is poured like molten metal into a new mould. That is the συντέλεια τοῦ αἰῶνος τούτου, the *consummatio mundi*, the consummation of this world.

3. *The Balance Sheet of the Present Age of the World*

We have seen that the later Jewish apocalyptic writers, who were the first to express this expectation of the end, born out of the depths of world suffering, were already quite clearly aware of the fact that it would be futile to try to envisage this perfect state with our faculties. Every attempt to depict the eternal in the colours of this transient world is subject to the dictum: "Everything transient is but a likeness." So long as we still find rest in such pictures as, say, the idea of a classless society, in which all persons have an equal share in the good things of the earth, or a reign of world peace, in which all swords will be beaten into ploughshares and men will live together in a paradise, we have not yet looked into the deepest recesses of reality. Only when all these dream pictures are dispersed like clouds of mist under the impact of such annihilating catastrophes as the world has experienced in our day, do we know that redemption is only possible if the whole form of this world passes away, and its place is taken by what the New Testament describes in the text:

> "What no eye has seen, nor ear heard,
>   nor the heart of man conceived,
>   what God has prepared for those who love Him."
>
> (1 Cor. 11.9)

Only when we have given up the attempt to penetrate the secrets of this glory with our human faculties, are we ripe for the understanding of the promises which are declared in lapidary sentences and with divine authority by the men of the New Testament, who staked their lives on the truth of these promises. In doing so they abandoned any attempt to envisage it, and only spoke of it in figures, when it was quite clear that these could only be earthly parables of what our eyes cannot as yet see.

The whole creation (πᾶσα κτίσις), they said, that is, not only the human world, and not merely the animal and vegetable worlds, but also the whole inorganic world; not merely our solar system, but also all the galactic systems which exist outside our own and which are all subject to the same scheme of this world, this whole creation will be "liberated." From what?

Not merely from the pains and sorrows which sadden our present existence, from the miseries of disease and the fear of death, and not merely from the social injustices which cause so much unrest in our community life, but from something which has a far more widespread significance, from the "bondage of corruption." It is thus a question of liberation from a form of existence which is comparable with slavery. A man who was born a slave and as a consequence branded as a slave from birth, lived in a lifelong imprisonment, without any hope of ever being freed from this servitude. Similarly, in the opinion of the Apostle, all of us at our entrance into our present existence are bound together with the whole creation in subjection to the form of existence of this world. The whole creation, writes Paul, is like a prisoner serving a life sentence, who yearns with every fibre of his being for deliverance (Rom. VIII.19ff.).

This situation will be abolished, the gates of the prison will be burst open. The whole of reality will be brought back from the polar state into that supra-polar state in which God is. Biblically expressed: "God will be all in all." The whole creation will be redeemed from the restless flight of time and will return home to the Sabbath rest of God, in which "God rested on the seventh day from all his works" (Heb. IV.4). This is not the rest of death nor the abolition of all distinctions, but the rest of perfection. The stream of time, which presses forward, will flow into the deep sea of eternity.

This abolition of the present world form will show itself negatively in that the rigid, fundamental law, to which all life in the present world order is subject, and without which we cannot imagine any life in the present age, will be cancelled – the biological principle that life can only increase and multiply by a process in which other life is suffocated and destroyed with pain and deadly torture. This abolition of the present law of life is implicit in the promise: "He will wipe away every tear from their eyes, and death shall be no more, neither shall there be mourning nor crying nor pain any more, for the former things have passed away" (Rev. XXI.4). That is only a negative statement.

Positively the abolition of the present world form is shown in the fact that God becomes visible. The Revelation of John explains this fact when it says: "The city has no need of sun or moon to shine upon it, for the glory of God is its light" (Rev. xxi.23). God will thus be to the whole world what the sun is to the world at present, the light in whose brilliance all things shine and which illuminates all things. God will be so near to us men, as is said in the same chapter, that no one can any longer doubt His reality: "Behold, the dwelling of God is with men, He will dwell with them, and they shall be his people, and God himself will be with them" (Rev. xxi.3).

As we saw, the polar world form, in which we are now imprisoned, is like an opaque curtain which conceals from us the reality of God. When polarity is abolished, the curtain is thrust back and the realm of the omnipresence of God becomes just as much a form of intuition, embracing the whole of reality, as is the present three-dimensional physical space which encloses the whole of reality. The limits of our present existence, according to Kant, consist in the fact that for us time and three-dimensional space are merely "forms of intuition," in which objects can become visible to which our thoughts can be directed. For "concepts without intuitions are empty." When the polar world form is abolished, this limitation of our present knowledge falls away. We can "see God," for we live in the intuitive form of eternity.

This all-transforming event of the perfecting of the world for which the whole creation yearns is, according to the New Testament, not a new act of creation, in which something comes into being which was not there before, but a "revelation" (an apocalypse) of something which had always existed before, but had not yet been manifested. The veil which is taken away in this revelation is the present polar form of existence. That is what gives men who are sure of this approaching end their world-conquering power even now. They live a double life. Among them applies the text: "For you have died, and your life is hid with Christ in God" (Col. iii.3). Thus while the polar world daily oppresses believing men as an overwhelming reality, while they are confined like miners shut up in a dark passage in which they must work their way painfully forward, they live at the same time in another realm, in the realm of God. In God's realm the whole of reality exists in a way very different from its existence in the realm of world time. For in God there is neither before nor after. In God everything, as Luther once said, is an eternal moment. In the realm of God, therefore, everything evil and demonic is present too, but it is always present as already overcome. In the realm of God everything hostile to God is present too, but always as already destroyed. The mountainous burden which at present still weighs upon the believer, is already lifted in the supra-polar sphere in which he lives simultaneously. The overwhelming forces which oppress him already lie vanquished on the ground in the realm of God, in which he already has a part. Thus in the moment of prayer, the life of struggle and weariness, of hunger and privation, seems to them something unreal, out of which they will awake as out of a nightmare as soon as the curtain is rent, and they will be for ever in the presence of God.

There are particular moments and experiences in which this double life of the believer is visibly manifested. Here is just one example out of hundreds which might be cited. At the end of the first world war a number of people of all classes of the population were kept as hostages in a prison in the east, as a result of the fortunes of war. Old and young, sick people and married couples, children and the dying; they were all confined in damp, dark rooms, with a little bread and soup made of potato peelings. The mood of the prisoners became more despairing every day, until one day a sixteen-year-old girl from a noble family was consigned to the prison. She had just seen her parents and sisters murdered, and now with a miserable bundle of clothes under her arm she was flung in at the prison door. From the first moment there radiated from this girl a power of peacefulness and readiness to die, which changed the whole situation in the camp. She did not speak much, but when anyone was seized with a violent fit of sobbing and crying, she came to him and seized his clenched hands. Then he became suddenly still. When women were knocking their heads against the walls and becoming hysterical with terror because their husbands had been led out to be shot, this young girl came, saying not a word, but sat down beside them and grasped their hands. And quietness passed into their restless hearts. Then came the time when all the hostages were brought out to be shot, because the other army had fought its way across the Dvina. When they had all been placed against the wall to receive the fatal bullet, the little, delicate girl stepped forward, fell on her knees, and began a loud and earnest prayer for the executioners, whose rifles were at the ready. The prayer was such that something happened to impress even the soldiers who had taken part in many shootings. Those who had been commissioned to carry out the execution threw away their rifles and cried: "Let someone else shoot them – not us!" A second squad had to be brought up, whose men had not heard the prayer, to finish the execution, of which the girl along with all the rest was, of course, a victim. All who witnessed this scene, mostly men whose trade had long been slaughter, had the impression that there is another kind of reality, which lies beyond the whole struggle between men and nations, and in which world-conquering powers lie hidden, powers which will one day perhaps put an end to all the wars in the world.[1]

Of course this restoration of the present form of existence in the world to the eternal realm of God, which is already omnipresent, cannot take place without a break. At this point the difference between the Hindu religion of redemption and the New Testament Gospel of salvation is seen with special clarity. According to the Buddhist view, after we have passed through many births which are our inevitable destiny, after the voyage across the "Samsara Ocean," we come to the final goal of entrance into Nirvana, in which our little personal ego ceases to exist and is merged in the undifferentiated Unity. The whole "I-Thou-It World" will then sink behind us into an unreal illusion.

From the New Testament point of view this expectation is a dangerous deception. Our individual personality, our ego, is not a mere illusion which will one day disappear, but an ultimate reality created by God and inescapable. We cannot free ourselves from it. However much we may feel the burden of this reality, which receives its character from the guilt of our whole life, we cannot shake off this burden. The polar world, which I myself as an individual must traverse to the bitter end, is therefore no mere world of illusion, which will one day sink behind me into non-existence; the journey through the earthly life with all its temptation is rather a very earnest and very real test of endurance, which will prove whether I am capable of the attitude exhibited by Moses, of whom it is said: "For he

[1] See Hans Dittmer, *Rast im Alltag*, Göttingen n.d., p. 140f.

endured as seeing him who is invisible" (Heb. XI.27). Only when we in this present world, in which we are daily tempted to regard Him as a mere phantom, nevertheless believe in God without seeing Him, shall we one day see what we have believed.

The form of temporality cannot therefore be restored to the supra-temporal realm of God unless a judgment takes place, in which the final balance sheet of the whole temporal world history is drawn up. This judgment must affect first of all the power hostile to God, which stands behind the temporal world form, the Tempter, "who leads the whole world astray," and who has used the present form of the world's existence to bring about our fall. Then all of us who have undergone this trial must give account of how we have endured it. In this sense it is true that "eternity is the judgment of time."

In this context we cannot discuss in detail how this judgment will be carried out. But the final reckoning, which stands at the end of the present age, is not, as we saw in *Jesus the World's Perfecter*, an end in itself, but only a transition stage and a preparation for the great transformation of the world, which is God's end for this world. This brings to fulfilment the word in which God's plan for the created world is contained, and in which everything is summed up which in all the sections of this book we have been constantly illustrating from different points of view: "For from him and through him and to him are all things. To him be glory forever. Amen" (Rom. XI.36).

4. The Final Condition for the Understanding of Pauline Eschatology

The disharmony which pervades creation takes on quite a new aspect when the supra-polar dimension is revealed to us in the form of an event which is not within our control. As we saw earlier, we cannot bring about this event by our own strength. It must come upon us without our co-operation. Only one thing is clear: this event must take place in the centre of our personality, namely in our consciences. At this central point we must receive a commission which constrains us absolutely.

Let us illustrate this by a few well-known examples. In Luther's life the decision which gave him a new direction took place when, during a heavy thunderstorm at Stotternheim, the lightning struck near the young man and made him cry out in terror: "Help, holy St Anne, I will become a monk!" The sudden danger of death which had come upon him made him realise in a flash that we human beings stand under the judgment of an almighty God, who has entrusted to us for a short time this life whose end we cannot foresee. And afterwards He will require of us an account of how we have spent every hour of this life which has been lent to us. This sudden impression of terror led Luther to the monastery.

A similar terror once came upon Saul when, on the road near Damascus, suddenly a light from heaven shone upon him. He fell to the ground and heard a voice saying to him: "Saul, Saul, why do you persecute me?" "I am Jesus, whom you are persecuting." "It hurts you to kick against the goads" (Acts IX.3ff., XXVI.14). Here also the impression arose in the man that he was utterly in the power of a superhuman might, which gave him an irresistible command. With trembling and astonishment he said: "Lord, what wilt thou have me to do?"

Already in the Old Testament we find again and again such calls and commissionings, under the influence of which a human life begins to change. Consider what Jeremiah says about the decisive hour in his life:

> O Lord, thou hast deceived me,
>   and I was deceived;
> thou art stronger than I,
>   and thou hast prevailed. . . .
> If I say, "I will not mention him,
>   or speak any more in his name,"
> there is in my heart as it were a burning fire
>   shut up in my bones,
> and I am weary with holding it in,
>   and I cannot.

(Jer. xx.7, 9)

When, as in these examples, the supra-polar dimension is revealed to a man by a quite definite concrete impression the reality which is thereby revealed to him may be quite simply summed up as follows: God is the Thou of whom it is true to say, everything that is outside Him, the whole created world, exists for Him. It belongs to Him. He has absolute power over it.

What follows from this for the situation of the unclean world in which we live, will perhaps be explained most quickly by the following argument from Anselm of Canterbury's well-known book *Cur deus homo*. If everything which exists outside God, exists for God and is subject to His omnipotence, we must draw the conclusion that if anywhere in the world anything, however little, happens against God's will, if, for example, a man casts his eyes on something against God's will, and so defiles his soul, then the whole divinity of God is thereby put in question. It is not the same as when, in the polar world, something happens somewhere in the realm of some king or despot which is against the ruler's will. To repair this injustice it is quite enough for the police authority or the military power to intervene and punish the evildoer. Thus the authority of the king is restored.

It is different when something happens against God's will in the world which belongs to God, something which contradicts that will. Then the vital question at once arises, for thereby the divinity of God is put in question. Anselm says: *nondum considerasti quanti ponderis sit peccatum* (you have not considered what a tremendous weight sin is). The tiniest sin means always an attack on the reality of God Himself, a revolt against the majesty of God, which must issue from a power – must be an attempt of this revolutionary power – to drive God from His throne and to set itself in His place. In other words every sin, even the smallest, has a Satanic character.

Now at last we realise what is the meaning of the disharmony which pervades the world, when we see it from the standpoint of God's omnipotence. The fact that any sin is possible in the world which belongs to God, can only mean that from the beginning of creation a Satanic power has been omnipresent in the world, whose aim is to drive God Himself from the throne and to set himself in His place. From this point of view we understand the sinister background of the New Testament view of the demonic world, which prevails not only over the world of humanity, but over the whole cosmos. From this point of view the passage in Rom. v.12 must be expounded. In the original Greek text it reads: δι' ἑνὸς ἀνθρώπου ἡ ἁμαρτία εἰς τὸν κόσμον εἰσῆλθεν ("Through one man sin came into the world.") It does not say: δι'ἕνα ἄνθρωπον ("because of one man"), which would make Adam responsible for the origin of sin and death, but δι' ἑνὸς ἀνθρώπου ("through one man"). Δία with the genitive means a point of transition, for example, a door through which one can enter a house. ἡ ἁμαρτία (sin) means here, not the general transgression of the divine commandments, but the Satanic power which stands behind every sin, and which from the beginning, soon after the creation, came into operation in the world. Of this Satanic power which stands behind all guilt, it is said that it penetrated into the world of humanity through the first man as through a door. The word "cosmos," especially in Paul, very frequently means not the universe, but the world of humanity. Thus here the view is expressed that the dominion which death exercised in the whole creation even before the creation of man is due to the fact that the Satanic rebellion against the omnipotence of God has been in force in the whole creation even before the rise of man. Only in this way can the statements in the eighth chapter of Romans about the whole created world (πᾶσα ἡ κτίσις) be made intelligible. For the yearning of the whole creation waits for the revelation of the sons of God. The whole creation is under a curse derived from the Satanic power, which has brought the living world of creation under the bondage of corruption.

How does this penetration of a Satanic power affect the divine creation and our human condition? In Rom. VIII.20 Paul answers this difficult question with a suggestive hint. The creation was subjected to corruption, he says, not willingly (οὐχ ἑκοῦσα), that is on the basis of its own decision, but through him who subjected it (διὰ τόν ὑποτάξαντα). God's creation has thus received a different basic form, which it did not originally have at the time of its actual creation, the basic form we have hitherto called the polar form. How did this arise? Not through a free decision of its own, but through a power which carried through the subjection to the form of corruption. Our whole understanding of the present state of the created world depends on the question: Who is it that has brought about this subjection of the creation to the bondage of corruption? Who is the ὑποτάξας referred to here? It was at first thought to be Adam, on account of whom, according to Rom. V.12, the Satanic power entered the word. But to say that Paul meant that a man, namely the first man, by his own action brought the form of death into power over the whole creation, is a view impossible to reconcile with the whole fundamental outlook of Paul as to the meaning of man and of the human condition.

This led to the idea that the ὑποτάξας, the power which threatened the creation with the form of death, is God Himself. But this view does not agree with what Paul says a few chapters earlier (Rom. VI.12ff.) about God and sin. There, in answer to the question whether in the new situation we are to continue in sin, he sets out the two possibilities between which we have to choose. In a military metaphor, the situation in which we find ourselves is described as follows: we have to choose between two conflicting powers or army commanders. One power is sin, which when we enter into its service pays us with death. The other power is God, who, to express it in military terms, offers as our reward the bounty (χάρισμα) of eternal life. In the Roman army, which provides the illustration here, it frequently happened that the victorious Emperor paid out to his legions a bounty for their bravery, which was something quite different from the pay which the soldier earned otherwise. The situation in which we find ourselves is thus illustrated here from a battle between two armies. The commander of one army is the personified power of sin, which pays its soldiers with death. The other army consists of God's volunteers.

The suggestion that it is God who subjects the creation to corruption, perhaps as a punishment for its guilt, does not at all fit this general view. It is rather a revolutionary power which opposes the army of God and pays those who enlist in its service with corruption. If accordingly the ὑποτάξας cannot be God – from God comes always only the gift of grace, eternal life – only one exegesis remains. The ὑποτάξας whom Paul refers to is neither a man nor God the Creator, but the revolutionary power of sin, which opposes the army of the holy God and recruits soldiers for the battle against God.

If this is the case, then only one question remains: how is this revolutionary campaign of the Satanic power against God related to the voluntary decisions of men? At first it would appear as if we might say that we are not at all responsible for our guilt. The guilt is borne by the sinister power, which

already existed before men and which simply brought us under
its spell by its tempting wiles. But here we come up against the
ultimate mystery concealed in sin. The sin which seeks to lead
us astray is, to be sure, a power alien to our innermost being,
which was created by God. To this extent the statement of Paul
is true. We do not fall into sin willingly (οὐχ ἑκοῦσα). But
this is just the mysterious riddle with which the situation of the
created world confronts us: this ultimately alien power, under
whose spell we have fallen, nevertheless dwells in our innermost hearts. The hatred of God, which is demonically expressed,
for example, in the writings of Nietzsche, is present also in the
secret unconscious of all our souls. "We will not have this man
to rule over us." There lies within us, however concealed and
as a rule strongly repressed, the urge to which the Prodigal Son
fell a victim when he said to his father: "Father, give me the
share of property that falls to me" (Lk. xv.12). It is the wild
longing for freedom, which every man knows from his own
experience, and the flight from the presence of God. Only
because this sinister hatred of God is somehow hidden in every
living creature, can we understand the prevalence of sin and
godlessness in the world of humanity, indeed in the whole
creation. It is like a subterranean stream of lava which constantly erupts into the world, and even in the animal world is
responsible for the cruel forms of mutual destruction. This fact
is the true expression of the fallen state of the world.

That is the reason why this created world has not only its
day aspect, which is visible to us when we look at nature, but
at the same time a sinister night aspect, which one experiences
with horror especially in the phenomena of magic and demonic
possession. One thinks here especially of the experiences constantly met with by many pastors, like the elder Blumhardt or
Seitz in Teichwolframsdorf, of which we have detailed reports.

It is characteristic that precisely where God's revelation in
the world is most clearly manifested, above all in the life of
Jesus, the power of darkness finds a sinister expression. And
how sinister too is the fact that men who perhaps have been
"converted" in their early youth, in their later years have to
withstand again and again the irresistible temptation to utter
blasphemies against God!

Especially Satanic is the phenomenon of possession, which

has been observed not only in the time of Jesus and His Apostles, but right down to our own time. It is the state in which a man is not master of himself, but utterly under the control of an alien, ungodly power, which rules his tongue and all the other members of his body. Seitz reports a case in which a possessed man was brought to his house in Teichwolframs-dorf, because all other methods of curing him had been tried in vain. Eventually there remained only one method to be tried, namely prayer. But when attempts were made to pray for the sick man in his presence, it only brought on another attack of frenzy. So they hit upon the idea of waiting until the sick man had sunk into a deep sleep in the evening, and during this state, in another wing of the large house, common inter-cession was made for him. In the circumstances it was quite impossible that the sick man could hear or otherwise have any information about the prayer taking place on his behalf. But at the very instant when the brothers began to pray for him, the possessed man woke out of his sleep and again started to rave and to curse. Possession is the form in which the presence of a Satanic power is most strongly revealed.

Let us next summarise once again the results of what we have said so far. It has been shown that what Paul calls "sin" (ἡ ἁμαρτία) is not, as we assume from our rational thinking, something like the sum of all human transgressions of the moral laws. What Paul means by this word, in Rom. v.12 for example, is always something with a Satanic background. The blasphe-mies which Nietzsche utters in his writings, or the curses of a possessed person, are particularly impressive manifestations of the diabolic power, which in a hidden and frequently repressed form dwells in the hearts of us all. It is the dark side of our nature, the secret hatred of God, which is responsible for all lies, adulteries, and cruelties. If sin were only the sum of individual lapses by individual men, it would surely be possible by means of appropriate police measures and the saving influ-ence of a living Church to restrict sin in a country and so gradu-ally to free it from sin altogether. But the sin which Paul refers to is everywhere present as a sinister power concealed in the unconscious of every living creature. It belongs, if one may say so, to the basic form of the life of every soul, indeed of the whole fallen world.

The same is true of that which Paul describes as the inevitable consequence of sin. It is summed up in the three words: ματαιότης (vanity), φθορά (corruption), and the pregnant summary of all, θάνατος (death). In these three words everything is comprehended which we have hitherto described as the polarity of the present form of the world; the relentless stream of time, the murderous struggle between the creatures, and the universal fate of death which prevails over the whole world, from the molecule right up to the stars, which are doomed to heat-death. Its most direct impact upon us is the common sight of death, which has led to the idea of death the reaper, to whom one nation after another, one empire after another, one human generation after another helplessly succumbs, until at last death alone survives as victor, while under his cruel sway the created world is transformed more and more into one vast cemetery. This is what Paul in Rom. VIII.20 calls the bondage of corruption, under which not merely mankind, but equally the animals and the rest of creation incessantly groan until now, without being able by their own power to free themselves from this chain. The whole creation, says the Apostle, groans together with us and lies in travail with us till this present moment.

This leads Paul to the unsolved question: Whence comes this intolerable situation? In Rom. VIII, as we have seen, he gives only one answer. The creature has not come into this state of servitude voluntarily; it has been compulsorily involved in this intolerable situation by him who has subjected it to this servitude. But who is this unnamed ὑποτάξας, who is to blame for it all? It is not God and not man. Here we are confronted with the final dark and insoluble riddle, which hangs over the fallen world like a thundercloud. It is absolutely hopeless to try to find a solution to this riddle for ourselves in any kind of mythology, such as the idea that a prince of the angels, Lucifer, is to blame for all the mischief; that this angel, who originally lived in fellowship with God, fell through his own fault from this blessed state. This is all fantastic mythologising, which does not help us a step further forward. We can only say that the world in which we live is no longer in that state in which it issued from the hand of God the Creator. The insoluble nature of this ultimate riddle of our whole existence belongs, like everything else, to the fallen state of this world. We can only add, as Paul himself does at this point, that this mysterious subjection of the creation to corruption took place ἐπ' ἐλπίδι (Rom. viii.20), with the promise of a hope. Of this hope we shall be speaking in the next section.

5. *The Easter Faith of the Early Church*

In previous sections we have explained the consequences of the prospect of the imminent destruction of the world, whether by cold or by heat, for our whole attitude to life. This prospect is like a blight on all our plans and endeavours, on all our thoughts and dreams. For in this case this world in which we are working is not an end worthy of our highest effort, but only something transitory, an episode, emerging from nothing and disappearing again into nothingness. The whole course of the world, which ever enchants us anew when spring returns to the earth, seems nothing more than a piece of music with a lovely and promising beginning, which afterwards loses its charm and in the end relapses into the night of nothingness with a shrill discord. The world lacks what is essential to every good work of art, a perfect ending. It appears like a cathedral, whose aisle is built right up to the roof, but is without a tower, and so has no crowning conclusion; or like the broken pillar often seen at one time in cemeteries, as a sign that the person buried there had no belief in an after-life beyond the grave. One may console oneself with the thought that the end of the world is still far distant; and yet one must say that, distant though it is, with every century it draws a step nearer. Thus it casts its shadow even upon the present. It reminds us that even the greatest words ever spoken in this world by thinkers or poets or prophets will one day be forgotten again. This forgetfulness is like a sponge wiped over a school blackboard, and obliterating all the words and figures chalked upon it, so that not a trace of them remains.

This is the mood expressed in the Old Testament in the first chapter of Ecclesiastes (Koheleth), from which Brahms took the text for his "Serious Songs." "Vanity of vanities, says the Preacher, all is vanity. What does man gain by all the toil at which he toils under the sun? A generation goes, and a generation comes, the sun rises, and the sun goes down, and hastens to the place where it rises. The wind blows to the south, and goes round to the north. All streams run to the sea, but the sea is not full. . . . For the fate of the sons of men and the fate of beasts is the same; as one dies, so dies the other. They all have the same breath, and man has no advantage over the beasts; for all is vanity. All go to one place; all are from the dust, and all turn to dust again" (Eccl. 1.2–7, III.19–20).

We should have expected that this attitude of radical hopelessness and despair towards life would have extended to the whole of mankind since the discovery of the law of entropy. Why has this nevertheless not occurred? The reason is quite simple. There is a hindrance which prevents the sight of the abyss of imminent total destruction from having its full effect. What then is the nature of this hindrance? We can best express it in a metaphor. In the mountains it often happens that the path passes close by the edge of a deep chasm. Any clumsy step may cause the traveller, if he is not immune from giddiness, to fall over the precipice. But now there is something there which prevents him from seeing the bottomless depth. A thick mist has spread over the chasm, which veils and hides from the traveller the immense depth beneath him, and so gives him an illusory sense of security. What sort of mist is this, which keeps us from being disturbed although we are walking along the edge of the precipice of nothingness, and saves us from despair?

Since Plato's doctrine of ideas and Fichte's philosophy of the ego many people live in the conviction that the objective world, the whole material cosmos, is indeed rushing headlong to destruction; but that we ourselves, who have this destruction always before our eyes, carry about in ourselves an immortal soul which is exempt from this destruction, and after the death of our body, lives on in a higher sphere. With this conviction that there is a second storey above the perishable world of objectivity, in which our immortal spirits are concealed, it is possible to accept the idea of the imminent heat-death of the world without difficulty, but only so long as this conviction remains firmly fixed in the general consciousness. Now it is the characteristic feature of our time, which was not yet present at the time of the discovery of the law of entropy, that faith in the existence of this upper storey of the world has broken down. The impression has arisen that the upper floor is supported by the lower floor of the objective world, and will therefore collapse immediately as soon as the lower storey suffers destruction. Literally speaking, the idea is spreading that even the relation between "I" and "it," subject and object, is a polar relationship in which one pole is conditioned by the other. As soon as this idea is generally disseminated, belief in the immortal soul and the imperishable ego will drown into nothingness. The whole mist-cloud which veiled the abyss has been blown away by a gust of wind, and the view of the depths beneath has again become clear. This is the origin of nihilism.

Any thinking person, once he has clearly realised the fate of the world inexorably presented to us by the second law of thermodynamics, cannot avoid a certain feeling of melancholy which involuntarily comes over us at this prospect. This melancholy feeling about the utter hopelessness and aimlessness of life and of the world then leads inevitably to the nihilism of J. P. Sartre, which is the prevailing philosophy of our time. Regarded from this point of view, the whole universe with its nature and history is nothing original and nothing conclusive, but only a transient episode, which has arisen out of the night of absolute nothingness in a moment of the past, and will again disappear at some future moment into absolute nothingness, leaving not a trace behind. Men as a rule escape from this mood only because they do not reflect on it, but are utterly absorbed in the present moment with its duties and pleasures.

Is there any way out of this nihilistic attitude to life? We human beings have no possibility of finding such a way out for ourselves. So far as it depends on us, we are a prey to this nihilism. If there is a way out it can only be offered to us from outside as a sheer gift, so that we have only the duty of accepting the gift and making it our own. Is there such a gift, and is there any possibility that we can make it our own? In Mt. XI.12 it is said of the time after John the Baptist: "The Kingdom of heaven suffers violence, and men of violence take it by force." Kierkegaard translates the passage: "The passionate take it by force," the men of great passion, who are ready with their whole soul to risk their life for a cause. This also applies to the only way out of universal nihilism, the Easter faith of the early Church in the New Testament. It is a well-known fact that living Christianity only bursts into flame in the world where men are under the pressure of persecution. Think of the story of the healing of the lame man in Acts III. The miracle of healing and the subsequent glorious confession of faith, that there is no salvation except in the risen Christ (Acts IV.12), occurs under the ban of the Sanhedrin, who afterwards threaten the Apostles with imprisonment. Or think of the persecution of Christians under Nero. Nero could not possibly have brought about this terrible maltreatment of the Christian Church, if hatred of the Christian faith and its representatives had not been widespread everywhere. The Christians were regarded as the *odium generis humani* (an object of hatred to all mankind). This fundamental feature of hatred of Christianity pervades the whole of human history right down to the present day. In China, for example, Christians are again being defamed as enemies of the state. The world cannot tolerate the Christian witness. It finds ever new methods and measures for driving it out and getting rid of it.

It follows from this fundamental fact that everyone who enters the living Christian Church puts himself in danger. In times of special tension to confess Christ means imprisonment and danger of death. And so readiness to risk one's life for one's faith belongs to Christianity. Only in this situation of deadly danger can it be proved whether the believer has a firm foundation and is really sustained by his religious convictions. Whether the Easter faith by which the first Christians lived is really tenable, cannot therefore be decided in a discussion evening arranged by people who live in conditions of security, nor in academic lectures, nor in learned books. It is decided, rather, only in the actual situation at a time of persecution, such as we experienced in Germany during the Kirchenkampf and such as may come upon us again at any moment. The words which occur in the second part of Ibsen's drama *Brand* are appropriate here: "Death is the rostrum of life. When we speak from there, we shall be understood."

The witness of the Apostle Paul about the foundation on which the Church stands is therefore especially convincing to us, because it is the witness of a man who was a long time imprisoned, and finally, so far as we know, was put to death by the sword for his faith at the time of the Neronic persecution of the Christians. We do well to pay attention to his words, especially to what he has written in 1 Cor. xv, so long as what we have to set on the other side, in view of the threat of death, has not yet been proved.

What is the content of the fundamental faith, upon which Paul with the early Church took his stand, and which sustained them in the hour of martyrdom? We need not here concern ourselves with historico-critical investigation, however important and necessary that may be, but only with a summary of the central ideas of his religious assurance. There are two facts, both alike of cosmic significance. The first is that the world, as it now is, is no longer in the original state in which God created it. As a result of the Satanic Fall, which led Adam astray so that he lost fellowship with God and wished to glorify himself, a Satanic power has broken into the world, which has spread like an avalanche through the world of human history, and has assumed more and more sinister dimensions. In addition to this first fact in the cosmic situation there is a second, which has likewise assumed universal significance: God has given authority to a man, upon whom He has bestowed His Spirit, to take up the challenge and fight with this Satanic power. In an unprecedented battle, in which in the end He was rejected by the whole world and hung upon the Cross between heaven and earth, He won the victory in the moment of defeat, both over Satan himself and over death, which he had brought into the world. Then as victor over death He rose from the grave. Thereby an altogether new form of existence has come into force in Him, which is exalted above the mortal form of the present world, and with which an altogether new creation begins. Paul is convinced that in this physical resurrection of Jesus Christ a cosmic event took place. Christ is, as Paul says, the "first-fruits" of a new, world-embracing event, which like the cosmic event of original sin must go on like an avalanche until it reaches its goal. The first-fruits, he says, is Christ; and then follows the second stage, which still lies in the future, the resurrection of those who belong to Christ. Then comes the third stage, "the remnant," τὸ τέλος, that is, the rest of the created world. Only when this remnant too has experienced the resurrection, is God all in all (1 Cor. xv.23f.).

This means, in other words, that the supra-polar being of God once more takes possession of the whole creation, which, owing to the Fall, had become subject to the destiny of corruption. The created world returns home to God and so returns to its original state. The argument here has been unfolded in greater detail in the third section of Volume III of this work (*Jesus the World's Perfecter*).

The interpretation of the Easter Gospel represented here differs from the traditional view. According to the latter it is concerned only with a fact which applies within the history of humanity. But Otto A. Dilschneider, in his important book *Das christliche Weltbild*,[1] has convincingly pointed to the fact that it is none other than Paul, the first messenger of the risen Christ in the Roman Empire, who from the beginning recognises the Easter message as of universal character and embracing the whole world. According to Dilschneider this cosmic meaning of the Pauline faith of Easter has only been preserved intact in its original form and further developed within the Orthodox Church. Even today this Easter faith is deeply impressed on the Russian mind, in spite of all the extraneous influences which have in the meantime passed over the Russian soul.

A little incident, which has no political significance but which does nevertheless shed light on the nature of what still survives deep down in the unconscious of the Russian people, may serve to illustrate this point. It was shortly after the Russian revolution. As often happened a huge mass meeting was taking place in Moscow, mainly attended by workers. The leader announced right at the beginning of the meeting that absolutely free discussion would be the rule, but that the time for speeches would be limited. A number of speakers intimated their desire to speak, and all of them delivered speeches setting forth impressively the well-known arguments for the materialistic view of the world and the victory of the classless proletariat. When they had all spoken, the leader asked whether the arguments on the other side might be represented. As had been said, absolutely free discussion was the rule. Then a little, under-nourished priest mounted the platform. While he was climbing the steps, the leader of the meeting shouted to him again: "But only five minutes, please!" He answered, "I won't need five minutes for what I have to say." Then he began: "You have heard all the arguments which have been brought

[1] Gütersloh 1951.

forward to prove the new world view. But my dear brothers, *Christos woskrese!* (Christ is risen)." It was expected that these words would provoke a devilish mocking laughter, in which everything would be howled down. Strangely enough the opposite was the case. From thousands and thousands of throats there burst forth the response which comes at the climax of the Russian Easter night service, when the fast is at an end and all the people in a happy ecstasy embrace and kiss one another, and spontaneously and irresistibly, like a stream that has flowed for a long time under the earth, all at once, like the lava erupting from Etna, the cry broke forth with elemental force out of the depths: *"Wo istino woskrese!"* (He is risen indeed). This little incident, which appeared in the German newspapers at the time, shows clearly that even if the waking consciousness of the Russian people is filled and dominated by all the arguments of the technological age, yet there still lives, hidden deep in their unconscious, the ancient cosmic Easter faith, which at any moment and on any occasion can once more unexpectedly break forth.

Even in our own day this Easter faith has burst into flame at the climax of the Kirchenkampf, when everywhere people were being sent to prison for being Christians, e.g. in the Baltic persecution of Christians. At that time the Christians in the dark prison in Riga strengthened each other for their last journey by a glimpse of the Lord who is risen and who is to come again, while outside in the prison courtyard the machine guns stood ready to shoot them down. This imminence of martyrdom is even today the situation in which the Easter faith comes alive.

The Easter Gospel which Paul proclaims is contained in the "mystery" which he imparts to the Corinthian Church in these words: "We shall not all sleep, but we shall all be changed" (1 Cor. xv.51). Thus he is speaking of a change in which all men will share and which, according to the previous verses of this Resurrection chapter, will not come to a halt until the whole universe ("$τὰ πάντα$") has been affected by it.

It will be a change which affects everything. Partial changes already occur in nature, when for example a caterpillar changes into a chrysalis and then is born again as a butterfly. Before that the creature could only crawl, but after this transformation it can fly in the air. In contrast to such changes, the world transformation of which Paul speaks as the great mystery will affect the totality of creatures which take part in it. Our human nature will not merely be confronted with a new objective reality, but even the subjective organs trained upon the new reality will be entirely new organs.

In our present state we can have no conception of this newly transformed reality. We can only say that it is evidently a new σῶμα (body), no longer composed of flesh and blood; but, as is stated in 1 Cor. xv.44, a spiritual (pneumatic) somatic existence will take the place of the present (natural) soma. The whole polar form of our existence, in which the corruptibility of our nature has its roots, will be transcended in the supra-polar form of divine being. This is implicit in the mysterious words in which the goal of general resurrection is summed up in 1 Cor. xv.26–8: When death, this last enemy of God, is con-quered, and Christ gives back the Kingdom to the Father, then God will be all in all. The world will thus return home to God. According to all that the Bible has already suggested in the Old Testament, so long as we human beings are in the polar state, we cannot see this divine being at all, nor perceive it in any other way without dying in the process. Even when we approach the vision of God, we feel instinctively that we have reached the limit of our capacity for experience.

For consider the divine vision of the prophet Elijah in 1 Kings xix. At first the prophet is still moving among the strongest impressions that we can encounter in this earthly world. There is the storm, which roots up trees and shatters rocks. Then the earthquake, and then the fire. But in all these experiences the limit of humanity is not yet reached. Now at last he comes, at least from the distance into the nearness of the "wholly other," who is described in the mysterious words: "a still, small voice."[2] Herein lies the paradoxical statement, that man in the presence of God hears a voice which is nothing else but absolute silence. In hearing this silence the prophet feels that he has attained the limit of the whole polar, earthly existence. Then Elijah covers his face with his mantle and enters the door of the cave. Thus do we stand, when we draw

[2] R.S.V. Author's translation reads literally: "the voice of a very soft or fine stillness."

near to the reality of the supra-polar divine being, at the limit
of our human existence. We must renounce any attempt to
describe what here encounters us. Even imagination is at the
limit of its capacity. We can only, like the prophet, cover our
face with our mantle and worship.

From all this we see that the attempt of man to penetrate
the secret of the end of the world leads us to two possibilities,
both of which embrace the total existence of reality. The first
possibility is the nothingness in which all earthly processes
come to rest, in accordance with the law of entropy; the death
of the worlds, in which the last word of natural science in the
future of the universe is contained. There is a second possibility
only if the universal Easter Gospel, which has been spread
throughout the world by the messengers of the risen Lord, is
actually true. According to the Easter Gospel the prospect for
the world is not nothingness, but the great world transformation,
in which the world will be delivered from the polar form which
is heading for annihilation. This deliverance comes about when
God Himself takes the world home to the sphere of supra-polar
existence, and the second possibility opens up, of which we can
at present have no conception.

It is clear that here we have to express ideas which have been
rejected out of hand in many circles today as mythology.
Naturally one can only express these ideas with the reservation
that in doing so we have reached a limit and have come up
against something which is not disclosed to our human thought
and imagination. Only because the Apostle Paul spoke of these
things with divine authority can we dare to make the attempt
to reproduce them in the language of our time. Perhaps this is
better than if we enter into the abstractions of existentialist
philosophy. The new and fundamental conception that Paul
brought us, and the only thing which delivers us from nihilism,
is the conviction that the resurrection of Christ is not merely a
miracle which happened to a particular individual, but the
beginning of a total transformation of the whole cosmos. To
understand and illustrate this fundamental new Pauline idea,
the system described as "dimensional thinking" is employed
in this book. We have been led to adopt this system, as in
Christian Faith and Natural Science (Chapter 11), where the problem of space in modern physics is discussed more fully, because

since the mathematician Gauss spaces with more than three dimensions have been accepted, a view which is further developed in Einstein's theory of relativity. If we think in terms of dimensions at all, it is easily understandable that Paul is reckoning with the possibility of a world transformation in which a new supra-polar space takes the place of the present polar space – this space of corruption.

We may here refer again to a fact which is characteristic of the situation and which since about the time of Gauss has entered into the problem of space. A long time ago a little book called *Flatland* by E. A. Abbott appeared in England.[3] At the time of its publication it seemed to be nothing more than the fantastic notion of a literary man who was trying to pull his readers' legs, and from which they would soon return to business as usual. Strangely enough this little book, hardly noticed at the time, has lately enjoyed a revival since the days of Gauss, Riemann, and Einstein, and has subsequently been read out of scientific interest, even by mathematicians and physicists. This book deals in the form of a story with the question whether there might not be creatures living, not, like us, in a three-dimensional world of solid bodies, but in a two-dimensional flat plane. The bodies of these creatures would be plane figures, such as triangles, squares or circles. The houses in which they lived would be enclosed by straight lines instead of walls and partitions. Otherwise they live like us as members of a nation and citizens of a state with a definite order of society. Now Abbott imagines the case of a normal man appearing among this community of flat creatures (whom he calls "Flat-landers"), a man like ourselves with a three-dimensional body whose whole manner of existence and world view had been formed in three dimensions. What would the result be? This three-dimensional creature would produce a tremendous confusion and sensation among the Flatlanders, because by his very existence and the opinions it would confirm he would turn upside down all the fundamental laws of the Flatlanders' state, and things would become possible, which according to their rules had appeared simply unthinkable. The man would in the end be brought to trial, and a bench of "Flatlander" judges would condemn him to life imprisonment for disturbance

[3] E. A. Abbott, *Flatland*, London 1884.

of public order, or else he would be sent to a mental asylum.

This strange story can perhaps help us to grasp better many things which are told us in the New Testament. The forty days (Acts I.3) during which Christ as the risen Lord had intercourse with His disciples in an altogether new form of being, are among the greatest and most incomprehensible things that have ever happened in the world. Those forty days during which He went about among His followers, are like a green oasis in the desert of world history, rising from a bubbling spring whose source is in another dimension. Let us consult the reports of the matter which are left behind in the Gospels. An unknown stranger accompanies the disciples as they journey to Emmaus. At their invitation He sits with them at table and eats with them. While He breaks bread and gives it to them, their eyes are opened, they recognise Him, and He vanishes from their sight. But they say to one another: "Did not our hearts burn within us, while He talked to us on the road, while He opened to us the Scriptures" (Lk. XXIV.32). It seemed to them as if a messenger from the other world had opened for them the hidden treasure-chambers of the ancient prophecies (Lk. XXIV.13ff.).

If we draw upon Abbott's story to explain this incomprehensible narrative, we should have to say that a man belonging to a world with more dimensions than our own can without difficulty appear out of the unseen and disappear again into the invisible world. Let us think of the "Flatlanders" and imagine that a man appears out of the three-dimensional solid world; and let us consider for a moment what that means. While for the two-dimensional creatures only two straight lines can stand at right angles to each other, the three-dimensional world is so constituted that, in contradiction to this, three straight lines can meet at right angles. The consequence would be, that this three-dimensional being in the company of two-dimensional beings could at any time vanish in the direction of a dimension which would be invisible to two-dimensional persons.

Let us take the further case, that a being should enter into communication with us, who lived in a fourth dimension; so that for him there would be a fourth straight line at right angles to the three straight lines which constitute our space. This four-dimensional being could without difficulty appear out of this fourth direction, which is non-existent to our eyes, and vanish again. The closed doors are only closed for our three-dimensional physical beings. A being to whom had been revealed a fourth dimension which we cannot see, would be able at any time to come to us out of this fourth dimension through closed doors and vanish again, and could do this without our being able to understand it.

When the Emmaus disciples returned from their journey and rejoined the circle of the other disciples, Jesus Himself came into the midst of them, and said to them: "Peace be with you!" He greeted them with the common and customary greeting in Palestine at that time, *Shalom lachäm*. But this everyday greeting took on a wholly new content on the lips of the risen Lord. He comes from the world of divine peace into the midst of the strife of this earth and brings a stream of eternal peace into this world. When the disciples heard this more than earthly greeting, they were startled and frightened, thinking they had seen a bodiless *pneuma* (ghost), like the spirits which appear at spiritualistic seances. Jesus with great kindness deals with this error and refutes it by showing them His hands and His feet, with the words: "A spirit (*pneuma*) [as you mistakenly think me] has not flesh and bones, as you see that I have." Then He eats with them, to give proof of His bodily presence, and reminds them of the Old Testament prophecy in which the suffering of Christ is foretold (Lk. xxiv.36ff.).

There is a third event, reported not in the Synoptic Gospels but in the Gospel of John. On the evening of the first day of the week, when the disciples were again assembled within closed doors, Jesus suddenly appeared out of the unseen with a greeting, which contains the whole peace of the eternal world. He then gives them, directly from the sanctuary above, the greatest gift that He can give, the Holy Spirit, with the authority to forgive sins and to retain them. Here a significant episode occurs. The sceptic in the circle of the disciples comes in from outside, Thomas the Doubter, who believes only in what he has touched with his hands. The wonderful thing here again is the kindly understanding with which the risen Lord deals with the doubter, by inviting him to make palpable proof of His

reality. At the same time He speaks the kindly yet reproachful
words which apply to all future doubters: "Have you believed
because you have seen me? Blessed are those who have not
seen and yet believe!" (Jn. xx.29). Overwhelmed by this love
of the Master the Doubter utters the words: "My Lord and
my God!" (Jn. xx.24ff.). In all these cases the risen Christ
shows Himself as the Lord, who with His resurrection from the
grave was delivered from the limitations of three-dimensional
physical existence and so was able to pass through all closed
doors. Bultmann, in his book on the Gospel of John, has
rightly observed that in these words to Thomas, apparently at
least, a faith which comes about without seeing is placed higher
than a faith which rests on a visible manifestation. The conclusion might be drawn that we later disciples, who are dependent entirely on the word of the witnesses, are on a higher level
than the direct eyewitnesses of the Easter miracle. "Fundamentally it was not the vision of the risen Christ which should move
the disciples to believe 'the word that Jesus spoke,' but this
word alone ought to have had the power to convince them.
There is implicit in the story of Thomas a remarkable criticism
of the valuation of the Easter stories: they can only claim a
relative value."[4] In these sentences of Bultmann a contrast is
drawn between the words of Jesus, which is sufficient in itself
to awaken faith, and the visible miracles of the Easter story. In
this view the actual situation as it appeared to the Early Church
is not correctly seen. From the standpoint of the Early Church,
the Word of Jesus only has authority because Jesus by His death
and resurrection has taken away the power of death and con-
quered the Satanic forces. The Easter events are thus the
condition for the authority of the Word of Jesus. The fact of
Easter cannot therefore be placed in opposition to the word of
Jesus.

That for the Early Church everything depends on the reality
of the resurrection, that with this everything else, even faith,
stands or falls, is most plainly shown in the record of the resurrection faith which Paul has left us in 1 Cor. xv.14-19. There
we read in the decisive passage: "If Christ has not been raised,
then our preaching is in vain [that is, it rests on an illusion],
and your faith is in vain [it has then no longer any content].

[4] Bultmann, *Das Evangelium Johannes*, p. 539.

We are found as false witnesses of God, because we have testified of God that He has raised Christ, whom He did not raise. . . . If Christ has not been raised, your faith is futile and you are still in your sins [for then the power of sin, which has come into the world through the Satanic Fall, is still powerful] and then those also who have fallen asleep in Christ [those who have persevered in faith in Christ in spite of all persecutions] have perished. If in this life we who are in Christ have our only hope in Him, we are of all men most to be pitied [more exactly: the most worthy of pity, because we have then indeed risked our whole existence for an illusion, which has been shattered]." Here then, everything is made dependent on the one fundamental fact, with which the transformation of the whole cosmos has begun, and as whose first fruits and beginning Christ came from the grave on Easter morning.

This new beginning, of which all who have seen the risen Lord have become witnesses, thus divided the whole course of the world into two periods, of which the second has begun with Christ's resurrection, but only after a long interval finds its continuation and completion in Christ's return. This second period is contrasted with the first by its fundamental form. This is implicit in the eloquent declaration in Rev. xxi.1, 4b: "Then I saw a new heaven and a new earth, for the first heaven and the first earth had passed away . . . for the former things have passed away" (τὰ πρῶτα ἀπῆλθαν). World history thus falls like a tragedy into two acts. In the first act, in which we still find ourselves at present, the knot is tied and a tragic conflict is developed, which reaches its climax with the crucifixion of Jesus. Only the second act brings the solution of the conflict, in which the complicated knot is untied. Hence, in the first stage, the world in every sphere is characterised by unsolved problems, both in personal life and in the political life of the nations. Only in the second stage comes the solution of the tragic conflict. The knot, twisted in the first stage and ever more intricately ravelled, is untied. "God will wipe away every tear from their eyes, and death shall be no more, neither shall there be mourning nor crying nor pain any more; for the former things have passed away." There is truth in the words: "Behold, I make all things new" (Rev. xxi.4, 5). "For the form of this world is passing away" (1 Cor. vii.31).

The contrast between the two stages of world history in which we are all involved, is still more impressively illustrated in Rom. VIII.22, where it is written: "The whole creation has been groaning in travail together until now." Here our human destiny is linked with all the rest of the created world and seen in a vivid picture. It is the picture of the painful and afflicted state in which a mother finds herself immediately before the birth of her child. She groans and waits in the intervals of her pains with anxious expectancy for the moment of deliverance, when the child frees itself from the mother's body and all her trouble is at an end. In such painful affliction the whole creation finds itself in its present unredeemed state. It waits anxiously for the moment of deliverance, when the new stage will be born. In the first unredeemed stage the creation lives "in the bondage of corruption." It is shut up in polarity as in a prison. This is especially evident in the flight of time and in the painful character of the I–Thou relationship, from which the lover especially suffers, because he cannot get inside the other person as he would like to, but the other must ever remain a stranger to him.

All this goes to show the profound contrast between the two stages of world development, the unredeemed stage in which we all still exist at present, and the second redeemed stage, of which the risen Christ is the "first-fruits." Now the question arises: How does the transition take place from the unredeemed state to the redeemed state, which Christ as our forerunner has attained and to which we may follow, if we belong to Him? This is the question which the Corinthians put to Paul when they said: "How are the dead raised? With what kind of body do they come?" In other words: how does the transition from the old to the new embodiment take place? Paul answers in I Cor. xv.35ff., where he explains the mysterious transition by pointing to the fundamental idea which here comes into force. This is the idea of transformation. "We shall not all die," he says, "but we shall all be changed." Transformation is contrasted with another kind of transition. This consists in the fact that a first phenomenon is annihilated, and then a second phenomenon is newly created independently of this. Such a transition could also take place, indeed, in resurrection. The old bodies might die and, independently of them, new physical natures might be created in their place. But according to Paul this is not at all what happens in resurrection. A transformation takes place. What this means is vividly illustrated by Paul from the processes of organic nature. Here again and again a seed of corn falls into the earth. Underground it goes through a mysterious transformation, and then grows out of the soil in an entirely new form. "It is sown" and experiences a resurrection.

If Paul had had our modern biological knowledge, he might have quoted even more vivid illustrations than he uses. The sperm cells which combine with the egg cells to form a new organism have an entirely different form from the growing organism. We can indeed to some extent determine which parts or functions of the growing organism the particular genes and chromosomes correspond to, but the whole process of transformation which we see taking place is altogether dark and mysterious. We are confronted with the secret of organic creation. Paul refers to the mystery of transformation which here confronts us when he says: "What you sow is not the body which is to be, but a bare kernel, perhaps of wheat or of some other grain. But God gives it a body as he has chosen, and to each kind of seed its own body" (1 Cor. xv.37–8).

What Paul here suggests is something which biology has thoroughly investigated in modern times: first of all the contrast between the germ plasm from which the new body is produced, and the utterly different form of the growing organism itself; next the fact indicated by Paul when he says: "God gives to each kind of seed its own body." Since Mendel ascertained the law of heredity by his countless experiments, we have known to some extent the exact laws which serve the purpose of assigning to each seed its own body. These laws are so exact that they can be expressed in mathematical formulae. But the process of transformation which takes place whenever a specific plant grows out of a germ plasm according to these laws, is still a dark mystery even to the modern scientist. If we wish to investigate it, we eventually encounter the protein molecule, in which a vast number of atoms circulate. This molecule is the workshop in which the creative act of transformation takes place, which we are here discussing. If we could inspect the inner processes of this workshop, as we can inspect the machinery of a steam engine, we should have mastered the secret of life. But even the electronic microscope gets us no further forward. The Creator has obviously taken care, so far at least, that inquisitive people like us should be prevented from peeping into His workshop.

Here we must stand in awe before a miracle of creation. Goethe once on a spring day found a chrysalis just on the point of being sloughed off. He held it to his ear and cried in astonishment: "Just listen, will you, how it knocks and strives towards the light! That must be what St Paul meant, when he speaks of the groaning of creation." The transformation effected in a caterpillar, which can only crawl on the ground, during the chrysalis stage from which it emerges as a butterfly, and with its wonderful brightly-coloured wings soars into the air, is indeed a particularly impressive example of the total transformation of which Paul speaks. Here it is true that *natura spirat resurrectionem*.

But now comes the decisive point, which Paul seeks to prove with this reference to the course of nature. He draws a daring conclusion from lesser to greater, *a minori ad maius*, from a process which takes place within the little relationships of the polar world to an infinitely greater total transformation process, embracing the whole cosmos and extending far beyond the polar world. If God, says Paul, within the little world which is under the shadow of corruption, can carry out such wonderful transformations in millions of living creatures that we see round about us, how much more will He deliver the cosmos He has loved from the prison-house of corruption, and bring it into a new existence. This is summarised in the mighty sentences in which Paul opposes the present time of sowing to the future age which is characterised by the resurrection of the cosmos. "What is sown is perishable, what is raised is imperishable. It is sown in dishonour, it is raised in glory. It is sown in weakness, it is raised in power. It is sown a physical body, it is raised a spiritual body" (1 Cor. xv.42ff.).

The beginning of this transformation of the whole body from the polar state to the supra-polar state arises out of the decisive event, in which the Saviour of the world emerges from the grave as first-fruits, in order next to deliver the human world, which until then had languished in captivity of φθορά (corruption) and lead it into "the liberty of the sons of God." This sheds a light on the nature of the resurrection of Christ. As the first-fruits of the cosmic transformation, Christ, as Saviour of the world, must be bodily resurrected. Only then can He enter with His whole being into the new form of existence delivered from decay. It would not have sufficed if Christ had appeared in a subjective or objective vision, in which, as W. Herrmann once thought, the memory of a disciple, overwhelmingly impressed by the life of Jesus, produced a visionary illusion while at the same time the body of Jesus lay mouldering in the grave in Jerusalem. For Paul everything depends, rather, on the fact that Christ emerged from the grave in complete bodily form. It is of the essence of a transformation that the first body, which is the subject of the transformation, enters entirely into the new state and that nothing remains unchanged. The witnesses of the resurrection accordingly report unanimously that the grave was empty. Everything depended on the fact that during the forty days when He came and went among His disciples Christ, the Saviour of the world, had indeed a new form of being which made it possible for Him to pass through closed doors and walls and to appear out of the unseen and vanish again; but that nevertheless He had the same body as before, only in a changed form, and that He still bore the marks of the cruci-fixion, the imprint of the nails on His hands and feet.

We of a later generation, who "belong to Christ" (1 Cor. xv.23), can therefore only have hope that, when our time is fulfilled, our whole being will be transformed from the corrupt-tible form of existence to the new incorruptible form, if our Saviour with all His being has assumed a new form of exis-tence. But to make this possible, it is essential that He emerged from the grave and left it behind Him empty, so that no rem-nant of His bodily nature remained there. Bultmann has rightly pointed out that this Easter miracle is unintelligible and unacceptable to the modern mind.[5] The reason for this,

[5] Bultmann, "Neues Testament und Mythologie," in *Kerygma und Mythos*, VOL. I, Hamburg 1948, p. 50. In this connexion we should mention that besides the attempt in this book, another attempt has been made to understand the disappearance of the body of Christ in terms of the laws of modern physics. But this attempt only goes to show that at this point science is at the limit of its possibilities. It may be summarised as follows: if all the elementary particles of which the body was composed, were simultaneously transformed into radiation, this radiation might have been so homogeneous and of such short length that it could pass through the corpse's coverings without damaging them. In the process of penetrating the stone

however, is not that the world view of modern man is incompatible with the ancient world view and its three stages. The stumbling-block which prevents this understanding is simply the Biblical faith in God, which lives by the principle:

> Our God is in the heavens;
> he does whatever he pleases.
>
> (Ps. cxv.3)

and not what human reason, on the basis of a world view and a natural law invented by itself, prescribes to him.

Yet according to what Paul writes in the second part of the resurrection chapter to the Corinthians, the resurrection is by no means more incomprehensible nor more incredible than what God does before one's eyes every day in nature. Whenever a new organism is produced, as a result of the combination of a male sperm cell with a female egg cell, a transformation takes place, which for the biologist is indeed an everyday occurrence, but which nevertheless is altogether beyond our understanding. It is the same when in spring butterflies emerge everywhere from the chrysalises in which the caterpillars have been wrapped. Here constantly an ugly grub, which can only crawl, is changed into a delicate creature, which with gaily-coloured wings soars into the sunny spring air. This creature leaves behind the empty chrysalis, in which it was enclosed as in a tomb and underwent its change, just as Christ left His empty tomb in the rock. Here too it is true that *natura spirat resurrectionem*. Even in the corruptible world God allows such miracles of change to take place daily; how much more may we reckon with His almighty power to deliver His children from the

door of the tomb, part of the radiation was transformed by the Compton process into the light which blinded the watchers, who thus perhaps suffered other injuries which only gradually became discernible. The radiation, penetrating to the centre of the earth, was gradually turned to heat over an area of about a quarter of a square mile, and its tremendous energy produced an earthquake which overthrew the stone. It follows from the theory mentioned above in Chapter 1, Section 2, note 9, that even a dispersal of radiation still has an unimaginably small but still finite probability of turning back into material form. The ideas concerning the appearance of the risen Christ which are most acceptable to physicists—though they differ from the view adopted in this book—have been set out by P. Jordan in terms of paraphysical complementarity. But this recent hypothesis is so complicated that it only confirms our impression that the fact of the resurrection confronts science with an enigma in which its limitations are demonstrated.

captivity of the corruptible world and to bring them into "the glorious liberty of the children of God" (Rom. VIII.21).

All these mysterious matters are beyond our rational comprehension, and all of them appear as pure mythology to normal thinking and from the point of view of the scientist. We can only grasp this reality when, in a way which we cannot bring about ourselves, God has become real to us as the almighty Creator of heaven and earth. Only if God is, can He produce by His omnipotence this transformation beyond our understanding. Even if we believe in God, it remains an insoluble problem for us, when and how such a cosmic transformation, in which we ourselves have a part, will come to pass. Here too our thinking, and even our whole scientific investigation, which with all its methods of research, is limited to the still unredeemed fallen world, is faced with a final, insoluble problem. When and how can this total transformation of the world come about? We must be content with the answer which Jesus Himself gives in the eschatological discourse reported in Mk. XIII, to the question when the end of the world will come, in which He takes His stand against all calculations of the future by apocalyptical enthusiasts: "But of that day or that hour no one knows, not even the angels in heaven, nor the Son, but only the Father" (Mk. XIII.32). As the decision of the time of the final world transformation is reserved for the Father, so also we are utterly dependent on His almighty power for the answer to the question as to the method of the change. And to this we can only bow in humility. The only thing which gives a hint of it is the statement in 1 Cor. xv.26ff.: when the last enemy, death, is destroyed, then will the Son restore the Kingdom to God the Father, and then God will be all in all. This implies, however, that the Lord will yet appear as Victor on this earth – before its transition to the supra-polar world – and will reign over His Kingdom.

So much for the matter of the new creation, which has been manifested to the witnesses of the resurrection of Christ. If we may once more summarise briefly the results of this whole section, we can say that the feature of this modern age is a generally prevailing nihilism, which has swept over us like a dangerous epidemic, infecting more and more people as time goes on. So long as German idealism was alive, there was still

an interim solution, protected against nihilism and seeming to
offer men an eternal security. This was the great belief of Fichte
in the immortality of the human ego. Fichte knew, if not with
our present degree of clarity, about the law of the deflation of
energy (the law of entropy), according to which the whole
universe is growing older and older and is doomed to end in
"heat-death." But he could say: "When the last sun shall have
shed its last ray, I shall nevertheless soar over its ashes, and be
what I am today, and will what I will today, my duty!" The
measureless sense of superiority of the little human ego, which
here finds expression, is no longer possible for us today; for we
know that subject and object mutually condition each other,
so that no subject can hover free in the air without being
opposed to an object to which it is related. But since this faith
has been lost to us, to which our great-grandfathers clung, and
with which the fighters of the wars of liberation marched
enthusiastically into battle, we have now become spiritually
poorer. Since then we have lost the religious conviction that
our soul has an eternal security in itself and will automatically
be translated after death into a higher world. This interim
solution, which has no need of the Easter faith, has disappeared
in our day. Hence we are faced with a final option between the
two possibilities which now alone are left. The first is the radical
hopelessness of nihilism, for which the whole course of the
present world is merely an episode, which appears out of
nothingness and disappears again into nothingness, leaving
not a trace behind. The second possibility is the universal faith
of Easter, brought into the world by the Early Church and still
living today on its witness. According to this Easter faith, the
course of this world is not a mere episode, but the prelude or
prologue to the new state of the world, which alone gives a
final eternal meaning to our personal life and also to the life of
the nations.

We all have to choose between these two ultimate possibilities. Our lives, our thoughts, and our work are moving in one
direction or the other. The decision with which we are faced
is very difficult. We are involved in a spiritual battle between
these two conflicting views of life. Every philosophy and every
theology, and even every political movement, must join either
the first party or the second, and must take full responsibility

for doing so. In an age which draws more and more plainly to the end, and in which at any moment the early Christian situation of persecution for the faith can again break in upon us, we must, if we are to lead people, have something to say to them which will stand the test of a time of persecution.

There still lives in all men the longing, to which the "Wandsbeck messenger," Matthias Claudius, moved by the sudden death of a prince, once gave expression:[6]

> Truly we here a land inhabit,
>   Where iron is the meat of rust,
> Whether in cottage or in palace,
>   All things are dust.
>
> Where we all uncertain wander,
>   And walk in mist and night,
> In madness and illusion acting,
>   And never see the light.
>
> Where in the dark we taste the sweet and bitter,
>   While round us ever and again,
> All things, all, however they may glitter,
>   Empty are and vain.
>
> O Thou land of being and of truthfulness,
>   Everlasting Kingdom come,
> How I long to see thee in Thy clearness,
>   How I long for thee.

The longing for eternity, which the poet here expresses under the impression of the transitoriness of this world, is answered when the Easter congregation, believing in a fulfilment, sings:

> Thou wilt Thy glorious work fulfil,
>   For Thou our Judge and Saviour art;
> Thou wilt man's pain and sorrow still,
>   O Holy One! Thy way impart.
> So shall the prayer of faith implore,
>   And Thou shalt give us more and more.

[6] Matthias Claudius, 1740–1815, German man of letters.

CONCLUSION

With the last chapter of this book we have brought the six volumes which make up this work to an end.[1] This work, the first volume of which was dated 1931, with a revised edition in 1934, has been published over a period of twenty-one years of changing political and cultural influences. It is therefore necessary to point out briefly the signposts which run through the whole work and make it a unity. Above all it is necessary to make clear the inner connexion which the first three volumes, which are essentially philosophical and theological, bear to the last three volumes, which have a more scientific character.

The aim of the whole work from the beginning was to proclaim the Gospel of the redeeming power of Christ to a world which to a large extent rejects and contests this Gospel. In these circumstances it is not possible to plunge *in medias res* with the presentation of the redemptive significance of Jesus. There must be some prolegomena to prepare the witness of Christ for modern readers. The whole of the first volume was primarily an attempt to give the Gospel of Christ a universally intelligible foundation. It started from the fact that anyone discussing religion today, whether positively or negatively, sceptically or with conviction, knows of a view which man looks out on while he lives in this world. This view, of which most men are still aware, is described as that which lies beyond us, which stands above us. Thus it is when Goethe speaks of reverence for what is above us, and Schiller says: "Up above the

[1] Der Evangelische Glaube und das Denken der Gegenwart: VOL. I, *Glaube und Denken*, Berlin 1931, revised edn. 1934, Eng. trans. *God Transcendent*, trans. E. F. Dickie, London 1935; VOL. II, *Jesus der Herr*, Berlin 1935, Eng. trans. *Jesus the Lord*, trans. D. H. van Daalen, Edinburgh 1959; VOL. III, *Jesus der Weltvollender*, Hamburg 1937, Eng. trans. *Jesus the World's Perfecter*, trans. D. H. van Daalen, Edinburgh 1959; VOL. IV, *Der christliche Gottesglaube und die Naturwissenschaft*, Hamburg 1949, Eng. trans. *Christian Faith and Natural Science*, trans. N. H. Smith, London 1953; VOL. V, *Die Wandlung im naturwissenschaftlichen Weltbild*, Hamburg 1951, Eng. trans. *The Transformation of the Scientific World View*, trans. W. A. Whitehouse, London 1953; VOL. VI, *Weltschöpfung und Weltende*, Hamburg 1952.

151

tent of stars a loving Father must dwell," or when in church the words "*Sursum corda*" are used. Even in pagan religions an Olympus or a holy mountain are spoken of, towering high over the earth. So long as the Ptolemaic view of the world still prevailed, which even today has not altogether vanished from the human unconscious, men believed in a region beyond the sphere of Saturn, the farthest of the known starry spheres, the Empyrean, the dwelling-place of God and the blessed spirits. Every schoolboy knows today that the old world view with its three storeys, heaven above, the earth here, and the world under the earth, is no longer valid. Nevertheless men still look wistfully up to the heavens, to the place whence they expect help in time of need, so long as the last remnants of their religious faith are not utterly shattered. Only now since the full effect of Einstein's relativity theory has been seen, is the three-storey world picture radically at an end, and for the first time, as has been said, God is without a home. In the first volume of this work we attempted to draw from the end of the pre-Copernican world view not a negative but a positive conclusion, and to point out a completely new direction in which the believer might look, and which remains closed to the unbeliever.

What sort of new direction is this? To see it correctly, we must start from the conditions of this world, which are immediately accessible to us. We are familiar not only with limited space, such as a room bounded by walls, a country enclosed by frontiers, an administrative district, a zone, an "iron curtain." Alongside all these bounds there are also in this world limits of quite a different kind. Mathematics is familiar with a "space" which is not indeed endless, but unbounded; for example the surface of a sphere, on which we nowhere encounter a limit because it returns in upon itself. This gives rise to a *new conception of space*. What we call "space" in this book is a continuum, infinite and enclosing all that is given. The essence of such a space-continuum consists simply in its structure, that is in the law according to which the contents are determined within this structure. The simplest example is the temporal order, which results from the arrangement of its contents in temporal succession, in contrast to physical space in which the contents are situated alongside and above one another. We are taken a step further by the omnipresent relationship between "I" and "It", the seeing subject, which cannot see itself, and the world of objects, which stands over against the seeing "I," as an illuminated stage is related to the darkened auditorium, for the benefit of which the drama takes place on the stage. That brings us to the strangest thing there is in the world, the mystery of the ego of our personal existence. The wonder of the non-objective "I" alone radically excludes the materialist world view, for which there is only an objective world.

What is the meaning of the word "I"? It is not our body, which in ordinary life we call "I". This body is only a dramatic show for our ego, as Fichte said, a play which goes on before our eyes. But neither is our ego our mental life, our sensations and imaginations and thoughts. These too are simply a part of the objective world, a more or less exciting drama played before us. All this is still not our ego. Although it is the most familiar thing we have, we cannot by any means look into the depths of our ego. This ego too is a space, in itself infinite, but of an altogether different structure from the whole world of objects taken together. It belongs to the nature of this ego that I can only see immediately into myself, but that all other egos with which I have intercourse are utterly closed to me. Thus we have discovered a new space, the I–Thou space, which again is subject to different laws altogether from temporal order or physical space.

Now, however, we come to the last and most important consequence. All the spaces we have so far considered, the temporal order, the plane, physical, and I–Thou spaces, however different their structure, have nevertheless something in common. As has been repeatedly said in this book, they are all polar; that is to say, the contents arranged in them mutually condition each other and can only exist in this state of mutual conditioning. Take for example the temporal order. Its essence is that no moment can be Now, without being conditioned by a preceding moment and moving towards a future moment. So it is also with I–Thou space: "I am, only through Thee." This common polar structure of all forms of space in the world now leads us to an important result.

We are all clearly aware of being inside this polar relationship everywhere, wherever we may be, and of being quite unable to escape from it. The remarkable thing is that this polarity of our nature and of our whole earthly form of existence is quite obvious to us, so plainly indeed that we even suffer from it. As a result the conception of polarity is quite clear and recognisable to us at every moment. We cannot evade the conclusion that if there is a space with polar structure, then it is of course conceivable that there might be another sort of space which does not have this polar structure. We cannot say more. We cannot go further, with our human logic, without going beyond our competence. But it is quite sufficient, if it is plain that this non-polar or supra-polar space is conceivable and that no objection to its possibility can be raised by our intellect. Everything else is reserved to that power, of which we must now speak.

From what we have so far said, everything points to the one question on whose solution everything depends, but which we cannot answer with the power of our own reason. Is what we have called supra-polar space merely given as an idea, or is it an all-embracing and almighty reality? Might not the universe be merely a phantom, a figment of the imagination, which will one day vanish like a bubble? The previous discussion about forms of space and their relations to each other leads us at least so far as to see what must happen if the supra-polar region should turn out to be a reality; for we have seen what must have happened if we had first been confined to our I–space, which alone is directly accessible to us, and if now in this situation a second dimension, namely the dimension of a Thou, should manifest its reality. A space, that is an unlimited continuum in which a certain structure prevails, cannot manifest itself as a new content of experience, suddenly appearing before our eyes. As was shown in the first volume, forms of space cannot make contact with each other from outside like objects adjacent to each other. A second form of space can only reveal itself when an encounter takes place between it and our previously accessible space. The simplest example of this encounter is the encounter between I and Thou in dialogue, in which the "word" brings about a mysterious relationship between the two spaces. The meeting in the "word" comes about when the same content, namely a certain sound, becomes for you the spoken word, but for me the heard word.

The link thus produced is all the more wonderful, because I and Thou remain as strictly separated as ever. I cannot discern what is within you, and you cannot discern what is within me. Yet in the spoken word a living encounter comes about; and in this encounter, for example in friendship, the world of the other is disclosed to me as a new, rapturous reality.

This leads us to the only answer we can give to the question how, although we cannot see inside it, the supra-polar space of God can be revealed to us in its inexhaustible riches. We stand face to face with the fact, on the certainty of which the whole Christian faith stands or falls: *God has spoken.* "In many and various ways God spoke of old to our fathers by the prophets; but in these last days he has spoken to us by the Son" (Heb. 1.1–2). "Jesus the Lord" is the theme of the second volume, devoted to the consideration of the authority of Jesus as Leader and the revelation of God in Christ. Jesus is the Incarnate Word through whom God has begun a dialogue with us men, which, once begun, can never cease for all eternity. The Evangelists have told the story of the earthly career of Jesus from His birth to His death with such childlike simplicity and lapidary force that this account has become part of world literature and can never be lost. When we read this narrative we have an immediate experience of the meeting between time and eternity, between the supra-polar space of God and the polar world in which we live. The Church of the disciples was so much under the influence of their Master, that it could sum up its confession in these words: "Jesus is the Lord." "In Him" they greeted one another, "in Him" they made their vital decisions of daily life. He was the Leader to whom their life and thought was dedicated, He was the highest centre of command in all questions of life. In Him and for Him they went joyfully to meet the martyr's death. In bitter conflict with the Roman Caesars, the representatives of paganism who were themselves worshipped as gods, the decision was thus made, that they must employ no weapon but must rely on this means alone. In accordance with the injunction of their Master they made a simple confession of Him before their judges, and then went joyfully to their death in conflict with the lions or in the shambles, in the absolute certainty that immediately after their death they would be reunited for ever with their Master and Lord in another world.

These numerous martyrdoms so convinced their persecutors of the invincibility of Christ that after a few centuries the last cruel persecutor of the Church, Julian the Apostate (361–3), gave up the struggle with this almighty power, and cried: "Thou hast conquered, O Galilean!"

The fact that God has spoken to us men in Christ, that in Him a real encounter has taken place between the supra-polar and the temporal space, is brought home to us in personal experience, especially in the fact that it is not at the high points of our life, when we reach the peak of our natural vitality, that we find the way to Christ, but on the contrary precisely when we have reached the end of our own power and are spiritually exhausted and helpless. Then a power is revealed to us in Christ, which comes from a wholly other dimension, and we experience what Paul means when he says: "My power is made perfect in weakness" (II Cor. XII.9). Again a familiar illustration suggests itself in this connexion. When the time comes for the young eagle, reared in a nest high above the rocky cliffs, to learn to fly, the old eagle first of all flings him into the air inside the nest until his wings are to some extent grown. Then comes the moment of crisis, when the father eagle flings his young with a daring cast out of the nest. The young eagle at first thinks with terror that he must plunge into the bottomless depths, but then a wonderful thing happens: he discovers with astonishment that the invisible atmosphere, in which he thinks he is falling into the abyss, supports him when he spreads his young wings. This deep ocean of air is a symbol for the supra-polar space, surrounding us on all sides, and gripping and catching us precisely when all earthly securities of the polar world have left us in the lurch and we think we are falling into nothingness. The wings we can spread in order to be borne by invisible arms are the wings of faith in Christ, who at the very moment of our plunge into the depths, takes us up in a miraculous way, and carries us safely over every abyss. The eternal security we find in Christ when the certainties of the polar world are lost beyond hope of salvation, is something for which the modern age can provide a negative kind of preparation, because in every sphere the former firm foundations have become relative instead of absolute. There is no absolutely valid morality any more, there is no firm custom to which man can cleave, no order of justice which is still universally true, nor any human authority such as the great monarchs and leaders of mankind once possessed. This collapse of everything hitherto sure and steadfast is a preparation for a new discovery of Christ. In the midst of the universal relativising of values which we experience in every sphere, He is the fixed pole amid the flux of phenomena. By His life and death He has become the victor over the power of Satan, and has thus at once miraculously solved that most difficult problem which we men cannot solve for ourselves, namely the question of guilt that burdens us because we have all somehow succumbed to the demonic power. As was shown in our third volume, *Jesus, the World's Perfecter*, the solution of the problem of guilt is inextricably connected with the solution of the problem of power in this world. But God has so ordered the history of this world, that first the all-decisive question of guilt is solved by the death of Christ, and then, only after a long interval, at the end of the ages, the question of power is also brought to a decision by a second coming of Christ. So the problem of relativism is solved in both the spiritual and moral sphere.

In the fourth volume and the fifth, which appeared in 1951, the corresponding transformation within modern science is now considered and described – how belief in an absolute space, still possessed by Newton, and finally also belief in the causal necessity of the whole world process, were attacked by the general current of relativism. Only a belief in the reality of a supra-polar space, which we cannot however grasp ourselves, and which can only fall into our lap as a gift, remains as the ultimate salvation of thinking humanity. And from this point of view we have now been dealing also, in this present and last volume, with the question of the origin and goal of all things, and so with a new view of the beginning and end of the world.

From this standpoint the whole course of the world and the whole history of nature seem to us a mere transitory phenomenon. If there is a supra-polar space, then this world in which we live can only be, as the Bible regards it, a fallen creation. It has its origin in the eternal being of God, but its form is determined by a power hostile to God, which has infiltrated into it. Christ is then the heaven-sent victor, who has conquered God's antagonist, the author of the corrupt form of the world.

The perfecting of this present world must then consist in the process by which God in His great divine love lifts the world out of its fallen state and restores it to its original supra-polar character.

The Gospel of St John, instead of the prayer of Gethsemane reported in the other Gospels, gives a prayer by which Christ prepares Himself inwardly for the hard way of death. In this "high-priestly prayer" (Jn. xvii) we have a great vision, reviewing the whole destiny of the world from its origin to its consummation. Jesus first of all looks back to the blessed original state, in which He rested in the Father's bosom before the foundation of the world. Then came the momentous event of the creation of the world. It was as if, out of the immense sea of eternity there rose an island, the world in which we now live. It is as if heavy thunderclouds gathered over this shining island of the world; for the demonic power, who opposes the work of God in ways beyond our comprehension, was determined from the first to destroy and mar the glorious work of His creation. But God employs no force to hinder this devilish work of destruction. He opposes the whole of the world's hatred of God with nothing but love. Out of this love arises the resolve to send into the world the One who alone has power to conquer Satan, not with force but only with the might of eternal love surrendering itself without reserve to the enemy, in order to conquer evil with good and so to glorify God even in death. This is the moment which Jesus in His prayer describes with the words: "Father, the hour has come; glorify thy Son that thy Son may glorify thee." Now Jesus, in this dark hour in which He enters on the way of the Cross, looks beyond all this to the ultimate goal of His mission and the future of the world with the words: "And now, Father, glorify thou me in thine own presence with the glory which I had with thee before the world was made." He thus expects that the Father will lead Him through all that He has to wrestle with, and will receive Him once again into the blessed state, in which He once was united with the Father before the foundation of the world.

This is the homecoming of the Son to the Father, still more glorious than the triumphal homecoming of any victorious general from an earthly war. But here it is not merely a question of the homecoming of the Son to His original glory with the

Father; for His victory over the Satanic power that threatened God's creation means at the same time the emancipation of the whole created world. What Jesus foresaw in His prayer before His death-agony is something far more comprehensive, namely the homecoming of the whole emancipated creation of God. In this process the hidden glory of the creation, which even in the accounts given throughout this book has repeatedly shown itself in a veiled form, but which we can already see behind the veil, in the sense that *"natura spirat resurrectionem"* – this glory will emerge in its full splendour. And so the verse from the hymn of Paul Gerhardt inevitably occurs to us:

> Oh! when I think of Thy fair ways.
> And all the kindness of Thy grace
> On this poor earth of ours:
> What will the life hereafter be
> In yonder tents of heaven free
> And golden palace bowers?

With this glimpse of the future that lies far beyond our human horizon, our sixth volume has come to an end. I am well aware what a great venture it has been to intervene thus in the battle between Christian faith and nihilism at a time when the spiritual conflict between east and west has also reached its climax.

The worth or worthlessness of such a venture cannot be decided either by a Church Council, or by an assembly of men of science, or by any other human authority. There is a higher authority which rules in these matters. Paul says: "The day will disclose it" (1 Cor. iii.12f.). And it is as if he foresaw the coming heat-death when he adds the explanation: "It will be revealed by fire." Neither the worth of a human society we build nor that of a scientific system we set up will be decided by men, but rather will a great trial by fire decide whether it is built of "gold, silver, or precious stones," or of "wood, hay, stubble." We can only close this work therefore with the hope that it may stand the test at least to some extent in the great trial by fire which the world will meet, and so in the final struggle which awaits us all, prove itself fireproof and enduring.